NEW PATHS IN BIOLOGY

WORLD PERSPECTIVES

Volumes already published

WORLD PERSPECTIVES · *Volume Thirty*

Planned and Edited by RUTH NANDA ANSHEN

NEW PATHS
IN BIOLOGY

ADOLF PORTMANN , *1897 –*

Translated by Arnold J. Pomerans

HARPER & ROW, PUBLISHERS
New York, Evanston, and London

Contents

World Perspectives

What This Series Means

It is the thesis of *World Perspectives* that man is in the process of developing a new consciousness which, in spite of his apparent spiritual and moral captivity, can eventually lift the human race above and beyond the fear, ignorance, and isolation which beset it today. It is to this nascent consciousness, to this concept of man born out of a universe perceived through a fresh vision of reality, that *World Perspectives* is dedicated.

Only those spiritual and intellectual leaders of our epoch who have a paternity in this extension of man's horizons are invited to participate in this Series: those who are aware of the truth that beyond the divisiveness among men there exists a primordial unitive power since we are all bound together by a common humanity more fundamental than any unity of dogma; those who recognize that the centrifugal force which has scattered and atomized mankind must be replaced by an integrating structure and process capable of bestowing meaning and purpose on existence; those who realize that science itself, when not inhibited by the limitations of its own methodology, when chastened and humbled, commits man to an indeterminate range of yet undreamed consequences that may flow from it.

This Series endeavors to point to a reality of which scientific theory has revealed only one aspect. It is the commitment to this reality that lends universal intent to a scientist's most original and solitary thought. By acknowledging this frankly we shall restore science to the great family of human aspirations by which men hope to fulfill themselves in the world community as thinking and sentient beings. For our problem is to discover a principle of differentiation and yet relationship lucid enough to justify and to purify scientific, philosophic and all other knowledge, both discursive and intuitive, by accepting their interdependence. This is the crisis in consciousness made articulate through the crisis in science. This is the new awakening.

Each volume presents the thought and belief of its author and points to the way in which religion, philosophy, art, science, economics, politics and history may constitute that form of human activity which takes the fullest and most precise account of variousness, possibility, complexity and difficulty. Thus *World Perspectives* endeavors to define that ecumenical power of the mind and heart which enables man through his mysterious greatness to re-create his life.

This Series is committed to a re-examination of all those sides of human endeavor which the specialist was taught to believe he could safely leave aside. It interprets present and past events impinging on human life in our growing World Age and envisages what man may yet attain when summoned by an unbending inner necessity to the quest of what is most exalted in him. Its purpose is to offer new vistas in terms of world and human development while refusing to betray the intimate correlation between universality and individuality, dynamics and form, freedom and destiny. Each author deals with the increasing realization that spirit and nature are not separate and apart; that intuition and reason must regain their importance as the means of perceiving and fusing inner being with outer reality.

World Perspectives endeavors to show that the conception of wholeness, unity, organism is a higher and more concrete conception than that of matter and energy. Thus an enlarged meaning of life, of biology, not as it is revealed in the test tube of the laboratory but as it is experienced within the organism of reality itself, is attempted in this Series. For the principle of life consists in the tension which connects spirit with the realm of matter, symbiotically joined. The element of life is dominant in the very texture of nature, thus rendering life, biology, a trans-empirical science. The laws of life have their origin beyond their mere physical manifestations and compel us to consider their spiritual source. In fact, the widening of the conceptual framework has not only served to restore order within the respective branches of knowledge, but has also disclosed analogies in man's position regarding the analysis and synthesis of experience in apparently separated domains of knowledge suggesting the possibility of an ever more embracing objective description of the meaning of life.

Knowledge, it is shown in these books, no longer consists in a manipulation of man and nature as opposite forces, nor in the reduction of data to mere statistical order, but is a means of liberating mankind from the destructive power of fear, pointing the way toward the goal of the rehabilitation of the human will and the rebirth of faith and confidence in the human person. The works published also endeavor to reveal that the cry for patterns, systems and authorities is growing less insistent as the desire grows stronger in both East and West for the recovery of a dignity, integrity and self-realization which are the inalienable rights of man who may now guide change by means of conscious purpose in the light of reason which is something other than rationalism. For the whole universe is one vast field, potential for incarnation, a quality reaching to incandescence, here and there, of reason, logos, spirit and through which we apprehend preeminent value.

Other vital questions explored relate to problems of international understanding as well as to problems dealing with prejudice and the resultant tensions and antagonisms. The growing perception and responsibility of our World Age point to the new reality that the individual person and the collective person supplement and integrate each other; that the thrall of totalitarianism of both left and right has been shaken in the universal desire to recapture the authority of truth and human totality. Mankind can finally place its trust not in a proletarian authoritarianism, not in a secularized humanism, both of which have betrayed the spiritual property right of history, but in a sacramental brotherhood and in the unity of knowledge. This new consciousness has created a widening of human horizons beyond every parochialism, and a revolution in human thought comparable to the basic assumption, among the ancient Greeks, of the sovereignty of reason; corresponding to the great effulgence of the moral conscience articulated by the Hebrew prophets; analogous to the fundamental assertions of Christianity; or to the beginning of a new scientific era, the era of the science of dynamics, the experimental foundations of which were laid by Galileo in the Renaissance.

An important effort of this Series is to re-examine the contradictory meanings and applications which are given today to such terms as democracy, freedom, justice, love, peace, brotherhood and God. The purpose of such inquiries is to clear the way for the foundation of a genuine *world* history not in terms of nation or race or culture but in terms of man in relation to God, to himself, his fellow man and the universe, that reach beyond immediate self-interest. For the meaning of the World Age consists in respecting man's hopes and dreams which lead to a deeper understanding of the basic values of all peoples.

World Perspectives is planned to gain insight into the meaning of man, who not only is determined by history but who also determines history. History is to be understood as concerned not only with the life of man on this planet but as including also such cosmic influences as interpenetrate our human world. This generation is discovering that history does not conform to the social optimism of modern civilization and that the organization of human communities and the establishment of freedom and peace are not only intellectual achievements but spiritual and moral achievements as well, demanding a cherishing of the wholeness of human personality, the "unmediated wholeness of feeling and thought," and constituting a never-ending challenge to man, emerging from the abyss of meaninglessness and suffering, to be renewed and replenished in the totality of his life.

Justice itself, which has been "in a state of pilgrimage and crucifixion" and now is being slowly liberated from the grip of social and political demonologies in the East as well as in the West, begins to question its own premises. The modern revolutionary movements which have challenged the sacred institutions of society by protecting social injustice in the name of social justice are examined and re-evaluated.

In the light of this, we have no choice but to admit that the *un*freedom against which freedom is measured must be retained with it, namely, that the aspect of truth out of which the night view appears to emerge, the darkness of our time, is as little abandonable as is man's subjective advance. Thus the two sources of man's consciousness are inseparable, not as dead but as living and complementary, an aspect of that "principle of complementarity" through which Niels Bohr has sought to unite the quantum and the wave, both of which constitute the very fabric of life's radiant energy.

There is in mankind today a counterforce to the sterility and danger of a quantitative, anonymous mass culture, a new, if sometimes imperceptible, spiritual sense of convergence toward world unity on the basis of the sacredness of each human person and respect for the plurality of cultures. There is a growing awareness that equality may not be evaluated in mere numerical terms but is proportionate and analogical in its reality. For when equality is equated with interchangeability, individuality is negated and the human person atrophied.

We stand at the brink of an age of a world in which human life presses forward to actualize new forms. The false separation of man and nature, of time and space, of freedom and security, is acknowledged and we are faced with a new vision of man in his organic unity and of history offering a richness and diversity of quality and majesty of scope hitherto unprecedented. In relating the accumulated wisdom of man's spirit to the new reality of the World Age, in articulating its thought and belief, *World Perspectives* seeks to encourage a renaissance of hope in society and of pride in man's decision as to what his destiny will be.

World Perspectives is committed to the recognition that all great changes are preceded by a vigorous intellectual re-evaluation and reorganization. Our authors are aware that the sin of *hubris* may be avoided by showing that the creative process itself is not a free activity if by free we mean arbitrary, or unrelated to cosmic law. For the creative process in the human mind, the developmental process in organic nature and the basic laws of the inorganic realm may be but varied expressions of a universal formative process. Thus *World Perspectives* hopes to show that although the present apocalyptic period is one of exceptional tensions, there is also at work an exceptional movement toward a compensating unity which refuses to violate the ultimate moral power at work in the universe, that very power upon which all human effort must at last depend. In this way we may come to understand that there exists an inherent independence of spiritual and mental growth which though conditioned by circumstances is never determined by circumstances. In this way the great plethora of human knowledge may be correlated with an insight into the nature of human nature by being attuned to the wide and deep range of human thought and human experience.

In spite of the infinite obligation of men and in spite of their finite power, in spite of the intransigence of nationalisms, and in spite of the homelessness of moral passions rendered ineffectual by a closed scientific outlook, beneath the apparent turmoil and upheaval of the present, and out of the transformations of this dynamic period with the unfolding of a world consciousness, the purpose of *World Perspectives* is to help quicken the "unshaken heart of well-rounded truth" and interpret the significant elements of the World Age now taking shape out of the core of that undimmed continuity of the creative process which restores man to mankind while deepening and enhancing his communion with the universe.

RUTH NANDA ANSHEN

Preface

BIOLOGY is advancing into hidden zones of life on a number of fronts. One advance takes us to structures beyond the limits of the electron microscope; another to the mystery of subjective experience; a third to the problem of individual development; and a fourth to the evolution of life as a whole.

New facts keep accumulating. Many years ago, Jacob von Uexküll spoke of this accumulation in terms of an ever-thicker snowfall, warning that the resulting blanket of white would transform the landscape completely.

Our elementary textbooks, whose job it is to present the new facts in some kind of order, are forced to use large-scale oversimplifications, which the impatient student, anxious to leave the lecture hall for the laboratory, often mistakes for the whole truth.

It is our intention to show that many of the "basic facts" are not nearly so basic as they are often made to appear, and that their interpretation admits of many alternatives. We shall pay particular attention to unsolved problems of biology, the better to see whether the answers offered today are real answers or whether they merely impede the path toward wider knowledge.

At a time when biology concentrates so largely on invisible processes, we shall try to redress the balance by looking anew at the visible form of animals, at their external appearance. We shall find that if morphological problems are posed in a special way, they will lead us to an assessment of living forms that differs greatly from the prevailing one.

Apart from suggesting a reappraisal of the intellectual foundation of biological research, this book also tries to determine the limits within which biological statements can be made at all. To do so, it will emphasize many aspects of life that have not hitherto been given the attention they deserve.

Many of the examples are taken from spheres which my collaborators and I have been exploring for many years. Hence it is only fitting that I express my thanks to all those who have co-operated with me, and without whose help many of the discoveries discussed in this book might never have been made. My thanks are also due to Mme. Sabine Bousani-Baur (Paris) who drew the figures, and who, for years, has actively participated in our work, and to Mmes. Marguerite Kottmann Nadolny and Magdalene Neff for their help in seeing the manuscript to press.

The paths we shall follow will lead us to the very limits of science. Those who reach them can gaze into a new world beyond. It is my sincere hope that, in taking the reader to these limits, I shall have shown him that life is always more than science can say about it at any given time.

ADOLF PORTMANN

NEW PATHS IN BIOLOGY

I.

Invisible Life

The Macromolecular Stage in the Construction of Organic Life

WE STUDY life from two angles: not only from the angle of matter, which we try to explore with all the resources of modern science, but also from our subjective experience of life. Neither approach can be neglected in any serious discussion of basic biological problems.

I shall begin with living matter, and quite especially with an aspect of biology that has lately been attracting a great deal of attention and represents a momentous step in biological research: the study of living matter below the threshold of visibility.

When I began my own studies during the First World War, the limit of resolution of the compound microscope—roughly 0.0003 mm. or 0.3 μ—had been reached for some time. To go below that, down to 0.1 μ, biologists had to use the ultra-microscope, an instrument that reveals the presence, but not the actual shape, of particles, showing them up like so many stars against a dark sky.

At about the same time—in 1915—Wolfgang Ostwald's *World of Neglected Dimensions* first drew attention to physico-chemical methods of studying sub-microscopic structures. As a result, many of us took up colloid chemistry, and colloid chemistry continued to govern our ideas on the structure of living matter until the early 1920's.

Then—in about 1925—new concepts were forged, in the wake of breakthroughs on two fronts. On the one hand, chemistry had begun to probe further into the structure of large molecules, and a new discipline was born: macromolecular chemistry, or the chemistry of molecules with more than 1,500 atoms. It threw a great deal of fresh light on the structure of living matter, began to oust the exclusive approach of colloid chemistry, introduced many new "hieroglyphs" into the sign language of microscopic biology,[1]* and had tremendous repercussions, particularly on biochemistry, biophysics, bacteriology and virology.

Within barely three decades, macromolecular chemistry has led to the creation of a vast industry producing man-made substances, and to a radical reappraisal of the value of what used to be considered inferior war-time substitutes. Many people began to think that technology was well on the way to reproducing living matter, and especially matter which in its particular effects was said to be superior to "natural" substances. The consequent prestige of "artificial" products had far-reaching consequences, and not in the sciences alone.

Just as crucial was the second breakthrough: the discovery that the limit of visibility—which, at the time, was considered fixed—could be pushed considerably further. By 1924, it was known that electron rays could be used in much the same way as optical lenses, and by 1930 the first electron microscope was put to work. Technical improvements since then, and par-

* Superior figures refer to a section of notes beginning on page 161.

ticularly after the Second World War, have made this instrument the basis of a completely new approach to the study of forms.[2]

What does all this mean in practical terms? We have seen that the limit of resolution of the compound microscope is not much greater than 1 μ. Further magnification—for instance by projection—merely leads to loss of definition, and not to the addition of any new elements. The electron microscope, on the other hand, can reach down to 0.003 μ—or to 30 Angström, as physicists call it.

Before the advent of electron-microscopy and of macromolecular chemistry, biologists had considered the cell the basic unit of life; now they could no longer ignore those smaller structures which Ernst Haeckel had lumped together as *moneres*—structures which have not yet reached the stage of cellular life but prepare the way for it. They began to study the fine structure of protoplasm, and then came across such new forms as chlorophyll grains, chromosomes, and even microsomes.

The new vista which the electron optics opens up is not only a magnificent extension of our power to see directly where previously we had been forced to judge by indirect effects, it is also a vista of an entirely new world, a world in which the gigantically magnified image of a structure no longer means what the corresponding form would mean in everyday life. With the electron microscope, we have entered a realm where the familiar laws of ordinary physics have given way to the different laws governing the behavior of atoms and molecules (Fig. 1). In other words, electron optics does far more than

Fig. 1

The construction of protoplasm in the sign language of biologists. The picture shows an early attempt to represent invisible structures. Below is a vacuole containing a watery substance and surrounded by two layers of lamellae containing a fat-like substance. To the right is a drop of oil; on top, a drop of fat-like substance. The long threads with their smaller ramifications represent large protein molecules; they form a network enclosing water and other substances. (After J. Schmidt, 1939.)

reveal new details—it radically transforms our view of living structures. It poses the problem of living forces and functions in entirely new dimensions, where cells are no longer elementary particles but highly complicated structures. This descent—or is it ascent?—to new levels of research is the most important consequence of the biological breakthrough into the world of invisible forms.

It was in Basle, where I am writing this book, that Johann Friedrich Miescher carried out biochemical studies of nucleoplasm and nucleic acids in the "milt" of salmon, almost a century ago, when the Rhine was still teeming with that fish. Miescher had previously discovered the presence of nucleic acid in the spermatozoa of other species. It took almost a hundred years before the importance of his work was fully recognized.[3] Nowadays, these nucleic acids and their compounds have become central objects of biochemical research. In particular, the study of chromosomes in the nucleus promises to throw a great deal of light on a key problem of biology: the self-multiplication of elementary living structures.

In other words, micro-biology has begun to look at the difficult problem of how the ultimate elements of living matter— possibly the genetic factors in the cell nucleus—are able to build up matter resembling their own with substances taken from the surrounding protoplasm. Without this self-duplication, life as we know it could not exist, and it is no wonder, therefore, that biologists, assisted by chemists and physicists, are expending so much energy on this hotly disputed question.[4]

No self-multiplication has so far been observed in media

devoid of another important characteristic of life—metabolism. Only in a living "environment" can the genetic factors and other plasmatic "elements" achieve the duplication of their own structure. Before they can create living matter experimentally, biochemists must therefore be able to create living environments—environments containing a large number of simple organic compounds from which the material for the earliest phases of self-duplication can be derived. Bernal's sibylline epigram: "Life is older than living beings" seems to state just that.[5]

Modern biologists thus study life at what we may call the molecular stage, or—if we want to emphasize the distinction between vital and physico-chemical processes—the macromolecular stage. The study of this, the lowest, stage in the organization of life, is carried out with the tools of physics and chemistry, not because the processes of life can be reduced to physics and chemistry but simply because these processes occur on a scale for which the "exact" sciences have long ago forged the best instruments.

This new knowledge of invisible processes has thrown fresh light on the problem of evolution, or the gradual development of living forms within geological time.

If a gardener discovers an unexpected variety of plant, or if a stockbreeder discovers a new type of fur, an outsize calf, a hornless race of cattle or goats, the basic cause is invariably a change in the embryo, *i.e.* a change at the macromolecular stage. This change may result from one of three sets of causes: mutations involving one or more sets of chromosomes; mutations involving addition or subtraction of single chromosomes;

and finally mutations involving parts of chromosomes—we shall leave it at that for the moment.

The stage in which all these mutations take place has its own laws. Much of what happens in it affects the world of familiar experiences in ways which are not yet fully understood. All we can say with certainty is that no mutations occur with the "aim" of producing specific results.[6]

In the submicroscopic realm, every genetic structure has a special environment. Biologists call it the genetic environment, or the genetic background, and it is against this colorless background, invisible to our eyes, that so many decisions affecting the structure of living forms are made.

All life, as we know it through our senses, has its structural and dynamic basis in this invisible realm. Yet how vast is the difference between the two, between, say, our own breathing and the intake of oxygen at the macromolecular stage! At both stages a host of complex structures is involved, but what a difference there is in the forces and forms!

We still have a great deal more to learn—and this is an important task of biological teaching—about metabolic processes in this invisible realm before we can hope to form any kind of picture of an environment so unlike our own. We are in a remote country, where other laws than ours, and a totally different language, prevail.

The exploration of this country will take us, in the course of time, ever closer to the great riddle of specificity, which is also the great riddle of evolution—as we explore further, we shall find an ever-growing number of experimental facts which will help us to explain what molecular distinctions are responsible for the differences, not only between plants and animals as a whole, but more specifically between, say, the dandelion and the poppy, or the butterfly and the bee.

How odd it is, this life on the macromolecular scale! There are no individuals here, since what distinct unicellular organizations we see may begin to split into two even as we are watching them. For by "individual" we mean an indivisible being that exists in only that form, a being that has a specific relationship with its environment, a specific set of experiences, and one that can preserve its individuality for some time—for days or for years. (I am not thinking of thousand-year-old trees, for plants are individuals in a very special way only.)

We are also in a realm where there is no death. The immortality which men dream up in their fairy stories is real enough at the simplest stage of life. Here there is nothing but constant division. If we ignore accidental damage or destruction by predators, there is not even aging as we know it—there is no end because there is no beginning, every phase continuing its life in the one that succeeds it. There is no death simply because there are no individuals.

Death is one of the hallmarks of higher existence. It appears together with individuality and represents a turning point in the history of life on earth—which began millions of years ago. Death appears the moment we have a structure whose complicated organs take it beyond the macromolecular stage.

We are face to face with the mysterious fact that all higher life began with a germ whose structure, invisible to our eye, belongs to the macromolecular stage, and which, at this stage, already contains all the formal possibilities of the final result.

What we call life in our everyday language—the kind of life we can observe with our senses—has all its roots in the macromolecular stage.

Let us consider again what it means when biologists say that the familiar forms of life, the worlds of the senses, are merely one fragment of the secret of life; that where bacteria and viruses begin and end there is a second fragment—it is indeed the primary object of biological research—and that the development of life from its macromolecular beginnings to what we may call the "apparative stage" is one of the greatest problems of biology. The "apparative stage" is the familiar world of organs: the intestines, the heart, the brain, the eyes, the ears, the kidneys, and the genitals. But although I have called that world familiar, I must stress that our view of it is rather one-sided—it is often seen in terms of technical activities. That is the reason why comparisons between living beings and machines appeal so directly to our imagination.[7]

The formation of "apparative" structures may be arrested at very primitive levels. Thus even unicellular animals may be provided with structures which can contract like muscle fibers or conduct stimuli like nerves. They may have vesicles that work like glands, and supporting structures that act like a skeleton. Biologists call these primitive structures *organules,* to indicate that they are half-way structures between the macromolecular world and the world of organs.

Higher forms require the appearance of at least one nucleus containing chromosomes—hence bacteria, whose genetic matter is distributed over the entire protoplasm, have not really transcended the macromolecular stage. The concentration of an important part of the genetic matter in a special nuclear apparatus is a step of the greatest importance in the evolution of life—on the one hand, it ensures the exact distribution of genetic matter during the decisive phases of reproduction; and on the other hand, it provides for genetic recombinations, on which part of the evolutionary process must certainly rest.

The formation of nuclei is one of the first "apparative" achievements—a kind of "apparatus" at the macromolecular stage. Hence it is its "invention" rather than that of the cell which must be considered the crucial step in the evolution of life.

The advance into the invisible realm of life calls for a new type of scientist. Biological institutes everywhere are trying to train students who are much better versed in the methods of chemistry, physics, and mathematics than their predecessors, and who, at the same time, are familiar with the wealth of living phenomena at the higher, "apparative" stage of life.

Deeper understanding of the invisible realm does more than bring us nearer the solution of the riddles of life—though that is, after all, the chief aim of all biological research. It also helps us control them, and it is this aspect of their work which the present generation of biologists finds particularly enticing.

Control of the greatest possible number of living processes is the aim of a growing discipline—biotechnology—whose discoveries are already being exploited on a vast industrial scale. As its findings accumulate, so the economic importance of the new discipline will grow, and so it will increasingly affect the allocation of public funds, the planning of large scientific enterprises, the choice of scientific methods, and the way in which scientific questions are being posed.

Hence there is a growing need to make sure that those aspects of biological research which are not in the limelight of public attention do not fall into utter neglect, that some interesting sidelights are not mistaken for the whole.

II.

The Whole and Its Parts

The Problem of Cell Formation and Organization

THE RECENT study of submicroscopic structures has led to a particularly important result: it has dethroned the cell from its former exalted status.

Though cells have been observed through the microscope for three hundred years, it was only about a century ago that the cell nucleus and cytoplasm were first identified. (The term "cell" itself was coined because plant cytoplasm is bounded by a wall.) Plants and animals alike have a cellular structure, and since cells were known to be capable of leading an independent existence—there are a host of unicellular organisms —it was quite generally believed that all higher organisms developed as a kind of cell colony, or multicellular state.

Attempts to interpret cell associations in this way led to many valuable results—and to some terrible blunders. At first, cell organization was compared to social organization—like men, cells were said to share the work between them. So self-evident did this idea of the role of cells seem during the second half of the nineteenth century, that many biologists ceased to look upon it as a mere "opinion," and turned it into a scientific truth—because they felt the need for a concise explanation, they substituted a deceptively simple fiction for what are, in fact, extremely complex processes.

Moreover, this fiction even began to color the prevailing views on human behavior. Comparing society with the "cell state," many biologists found that individual cells were far more disciplined than individual men and played a far greater part in ensuring the welfare of the whole. Thus, what had been a biological oversimplification became a means of suppressing the freedom of the individual—the cell state became the dictators' avowed ideal.

The idea of the cell state has also been used to explain a host of purely biological phenomena. Thus, most school books describe one of the most complex and beautiful manifestations of marine life—siphonophores, whose organs look like medusae or polyps—as free-swimming colonies sharing all the work between them. Those, however, who take the trouble of consulting the all too few experts on the subject, will find that this simple view is not only highly questionable, but actually obscures the real problem of siphonophore organization.[1]

What then is the correct view of the individual cell and of cell organization? After all, cells are not mere figments of the imagination but reflect a biological reality. To get an answer, we must first make a slight detour.

We know some unicellular animals, for instance relatives of *Paramecium* (Fig. 2) which, though they grow to a size of one millimeter or even more, nevertheless have only a single nucleus (sometimes associated with a kind of satellite nucleus governing their reproduction). On the other hand, many other organisms of the same size, for instance the sweet-water rotifers, are constructed of hundreds of cells. In both cases, the same size, the same viability, a comparable degree of adaptability, and yet—how vast a difference in structure!

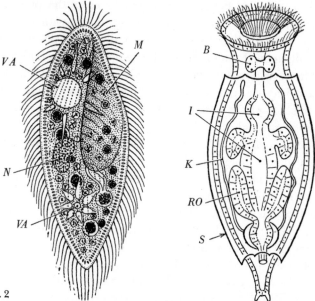

Fig. 2

Paramecium (left) and a rotifer (right). Though comparable in size they are equipped with quite different nucleate organs.

$$K = Kidney$$
$$B = Brain$$
$$I = Intestine$$
$$M = Mouth$$
$$N = Nucleus$$
$$RO = Reproductive \ organ$$
$$S = Shell$$
$$VA = Pulsating \ vacuole$$

We know algae that grow to a length of many inches—for instance some species of the umbrella-shaped *Acetabularia*

(Fig. 3), found in the warmer oceans. All of them have a single cell with a large nucleus embedded in a kind of network at the right of the "foot." But despite their single nucleus, these algae have so complicated a structure that they have become a favorite subject of experimental studies to determine

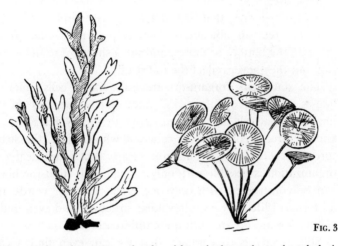

Fig. 3

Even complex algae can make do with a single nucleus. *Acetabularia* (right) with its single nucleus has a much more complicated structure than the brown alga (left) with its large number of nucleate cells.

the precise relationship between the nucleus and the surrounding protoplasm. As far as we are concerned, however, we shall merely note that individual forms with one nucleus can be as complex as structures with a great many nuclei—in other words, that complicated structure need not necessarily be associated with multicellular organization. This brings us back to the subject of cells as the basic elements of higher life.

When I say that all higher organisms are built up of cells, I express a widespread view which few would care to challenge. Another way in which I could put it is: cells are the bricks of organic life.

No one will deny that, in order to master complex processes, we need great simplifications. They help all those who cannot go on to the bottom of things, and are a short cut to those who can, but they never reflect the full reality.

The statement "organisms are built up of cells much as houses are built up of bricks" immediately conjures up the image of relatively independent elements, with which some unknown forces "construct" a coherent whole. Now, the structure of *Acetabularia* has shown us clearly that a high degree of organization is possible with only a single cell—that the house can be constructed with only one brick. In other words, not all forms of life have a multicellular structure, and even multicellular organisms are built quite differently from houses.

Still, reality is so complex that we can even find a case which demonstrates the brick analogy. We shall look at it more closely, precisely because it is so exceptional and hence poses so many special problems.

I am referring to a small group of amoeboid animals, the Acrasiales, which are often lumped together with the Mycetozoa as slime molds, even though van Tieghem had shown in 1880 that the two were quite distinct.[2] For whereas the former combine into large aggregations of free-living amoebae, the latter fuse into a single, multinucleate protoplasmic mass, the so-called plasmodium.

When Acrasiales come to the end of their food supply, the separate cells press together more closely, until they turn into a kind of worm, which starts to migrate over short distances. Then the cell mass "culminates," *i.e.* one end of it rears up, and forms a sporangium, or spore case, whose shape differs from species to species. During the formation of this reproductive organ, the individual cells participating in the process assume different functions and are modified accordingly: some become stalk cells which secrete cellulose and finally die off; others form spore cells, which form a tough capsule, and later serve the propagation of the species. Each spore turns into a tiny amoeba, which divides to produce new groups of cells, and these combine with the descendants of other spores. No sexual processes (fusion of cells with reduction in the number of chromosomes) have so far been observed in Acrasiales (Fig. 4).

Mycetozoa follow a different path of development. Here the starting point is always a sexual act: every spore germinates to produce a flagellated cell; two of these combine into a new cell; the nucleus divides without corresponding cell cleavages, and the protoplasmic mass expands and feeds on humus, or rotten wood and leaves. This mass, too, forms sporangia whose forms are typical of the species from which they spring. But unlike the "fruiting bodies" of Acrasiales, the sporangia of Mycetozoa are produced by the protoplasmic mass as a whole; they result from protoplasmic differentiation, in the course of which specific regions develop into the complicated "fruiting body." Mycetozoa represent the structural type characteristic of all higher organisms.

The comparison of Acrasiales and Mycetozoa poses the problem of the origin of the higher forms of life, but does not

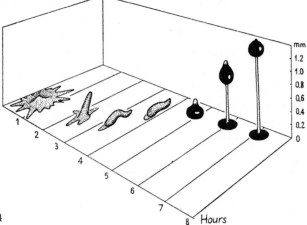

FIG. 4

The three phases—aggregation, migration, and culmination—in the development of *Dyctyostelium discoideum,* one of many species of Acrasiales. The sporangium—the name stems from the time when Acrasiales were classified as plants—is an excellent illustration of what I have called "self-expression." (After J. T. Bonner, 1959.)

solve it. The multicellular higher forms of life are not mere aggregates of elementary partners.

In order to describe the structure of these higher forms, we shall have to start from fresh premises, and perfect them as we go along. At first, we shall put it very simply as follows: all living matter is capable of self-multiplication and self-differentiation into higher structures.

Recent research has drawn renewed attention to this formulation, which was first used by Martin Heidenhain some sixty years ago.[3] What Heidenhain called "diachoresis" was, in fact, closely connected with what we have called self-multiplication and self-differentiation.

Now, self-differentiation is a crucial phenomenon of life, and cell-differentiation is only one of its many aspects. Hence it is important to know what precisely we mean by differentiation, and to that purpose we shall now look at the development of the fly embryo.

The fertilized egg of the fly contains a great deal of yolk—only a marginal area consists of relatively pure protoplasm. At the center lies the nucleus, surrounded by another small area of yolk-free protoplasm, and provided with the number of chromosomes characteristic of the species. The nucleus divides, and further nuclear divisions follow—but nowhere does any kind of "cell" appear. Only later do different areas of the protoplasm separate out round the new nuclei; cells appear later still, and even then they are absent in the region of the central yolk mass.

This early phase must strike us as very odd, particularly if we adhere to the brick hypothesis—instead of the bricks constructing the building, the building itself creates its own invisible bricks which start multiplying on the site.

Moreover, we can destroy germinal zones in the protoplasm, for instance by cauterization or radiation, even before any nucleus has entered these zones.[4] If we do so, we produce

limited defects—germs lacking a certain organ but with every-
thing else in place. In other words, we can affect the development of an organ long before it has any kind of cell structure.
Cell formation comes later and can be relatively independent
of the other embryological processes. Only because the pre-
sumptive organs (of other insects) are laid down after cell
division has occurred, has the wrong impression arisen that
cell structure is a prerequisite of organ formation.

We know from other experiments that, in cases where the
process of cell-differentiation can be prevented altogether, the
protoplasm nevertheless organizes the same forms it would
normally have built up of separate cells. For instance, we can
centrifuge the eggs of marine worms to produce larvae which,
in the absence of cells, nevertheless have a number of typical
protoplasmic structures in the normal place.[5]

Differentiation—the formation of separate parts in a whole
—is a far more characteristic phenomenon of life than cell
formation. Even when differentiation goes hand in hand with
cell structure, it remains the overriding principle—a principle
that can use different methods for different constructions.

Embryological experiments—particularly by H. Spemann—
have shown that, in vertebrates, the development of organs
and the formation of cells are two quite separate processes,
each obeying its own laws.[6] We have already mentioned the
fact that cell division, and especially division of the nucleus,
are observable phenomena, and hence readily interpreted. The
formation of the organs, on the other hand, and differentiation
in general, begins in the invisible realm and is therefore far
too often neglected. In many types of embryonic development,

for instance in the spiral segmentation of many invertebrates, cell divisions are so regular that they are often mistaken for organ differentiation, when, in fact, organ differentiation is quite independent of cell division. The larvae we obtain by centrifuging eggs are another case in which organ differentiation looks most deceptively like cell division.

The conspicuous reproduction of nuclei ought to have suggested a re-examination of the cell-state theory. To show why this is so, we shall now examine a group of unicellular flagellates which live in the intestines of higher animals[7] (Fig. 5).

They have a shape and organization which are in complete accord with the cell concept—each has a nucleus, a system of flagellae or of undulating membranes, a parabasal apparatus, and an axostyle. But, next to these forms, we also find others in which a number of nuclei is ranged round the periphery, each with a flagellum, a parabasal apparatus, and an axostyle of its own. Finally, there are some with more nuclei than parabasal structures or vice versa.

Though all these types are unicellular, we must not let nomenclature obscure the fact that they reflect quite distinct processes of differentiation. Once again, the familiar cell concept breaks down—the facts are expressed much better if we speak of distinct levels of protoplasmic differentiation.

Moreover, experimental studies have shown that not only the processes of cell division, but those of nuclear division as well, are relatively independent of the invisible processes of protoplasmic differentiation.

Once again we shall use the egg of an insect as our example;

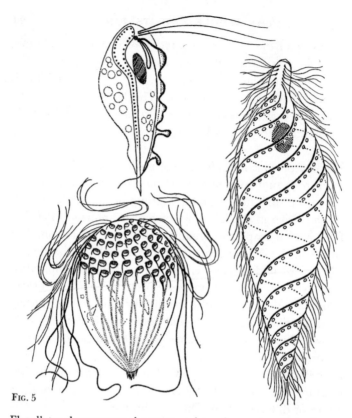

Fig. 5

Flagellates demonstrate the great variety of ways in which elementary macromolecular structures can divide and combine. The diagram depicts three parasytic types: *Trichomonas* (top left) combines a nucleus, a parabasal apparatus, an axostyle and a system of flagellae into a single unit; *Spirotrichonympha* (right) has a single nucleus, while the other parts are distributed in a large number of spirals; *Metacoronympha* (lower left) has all the parts of *Trichomonas* arranged into a number of equivalent organs. (After Grassé, *Traité de Zoologie*, Vol. I, 1952.)

this time that of the dragon fly.[8] In the early stages of development, when only two nuclei are present, it is possible to destroy one with a very fine ultra-violet beam without thereby damaging the rest of the germ. This experiment enables us to answer the important question whether or not protoplasmic differentiation depends on nuclear division.

If the nucleus is organ-specific, then all the "descendants" of the nucleus we have killed in our experiment must differ from those of the unimpaired nucleus—there must be a defect in one half of the egg. But experiments show that no such defect results. The remaining nucleus undergoes an extra division and supplies both halves of the egg with its descendants. The result is a normal larva in every respect. From this and many similar experiments, we know that nuclei are serial structures, all equivalent, and all isopotent—capable of replacing one another in the germ. Though nuclei play an essential part in embryonic development, it is the differentiation of the cytoplasm which ensures that nuclei produce different effects in different zones of the germ.

We have already said that the formation of the nucleus is a crucial step of nature, a brilliant solution of the problem of how to supply identical material to all parts of the body and especially to the germ cells. Cytoplasmic differentiation relies on nuclear processes, but is quite independent of, and quite different from nuclear division.

Our examination of microscopic structures and their formation below the threshold of visibility, has led us to the very core of the problem of embryonic development.

While differentiation is thus a far more comprehensive concept than cell cleavage, we must remember that differentiation, too, is no real explanation of embryonic processes, but merely a description. Indeed, it is the very purpose of this descriptive term to break through the barrier which was erected by the glib doctrine of the cell state. Whenever we speak of differentiation, we speak of a process whose effects have not yet been explained, and thus remember that vast realms have still to be explored.

Rejecting the doctrine of the cell state is not tantamount to rejecting cytology, which remains an important branch of biology, though with a more limited scope than was previously believed.[9]

A large part of our investigation of submicroscopic structures can be called plasmology or nucleology rather than cytology. The earliest apparative stage has many structural possibilities of which the "classical" uninucleate organization of the unicellular organism is but one, and one, moreover, which frequently displays multinucleate phases in the course of its life cycle, the uninucleate phase being usually restricted to the reproductive period. That is the reason why many biologists have long ago shifted their attention from the cell to the *energid*—the nucleus *plus* the cytoplasm it controls—and why they distinguish between mono- and polyenergid stages of "apparative life."

Higher apparative stages can be built on the monoenergid pattern—*Acetabularia* is a case in point—or on the polyenergid pattern (a number of nuclei with a common cytoplasm or, more commonly, separate nuclei each with its own cytoplasm and each surrounded by a separate cell wall). Now this pattern can either appear in the whole organism, or else it can be left out of individual tissues to give rise, for instance, to intercellular areas. In short, those of us who have delved into the complexities of histology (the study of organic tissues) know that many higher organisms are constructed in a way that no cell-state theory could possibly explain.

The important "invention" of the cell nucleus seemed to offer a complete answer to the question of how hereditary characters can be handed down by simple self-duplication, *i.e.,* how a genetic "code" can be transmitted piecemeal during cell cleavage. It has yet another important consequence. We know today that genetic processes are subject to permanent changes—to mutations, which lead to the emergence of new forms—and that those species of plants and animals have gained the upper hand which have somehow managed to consolidate the results of beneficial mutations.

One of the best ways of producing such consolidations is sexual reproduction, and that is precisely the reason why sexuality is so ubiquitous in both the plant and the animal kingdoms. Sexuality is first of all a nuclear and hence a macromolecular process. The combination of genetic material from two different sources ensures the emergence and subsequent combination of new variations, and hence the appearance and preservation of viable forms of higher life.[10]

The part which the nucleus plays in all this lends it a significance which, again, is far greater than that of the "cell," for though sexual reproduction invariably involves the fusion of two nuclei, this does not mean that two cells must necessarily be involved. The pollen grains of higher plants, for instance, have a multicellular structure, and some "egg cells" of animals contain a number of previously "digested" cells, which provide the embryo with food. The ovum of many polyps is multicellular.

What alone is crucial in the sexual act is the division of two sets of chromosomes into two identical halves, and their subsequent combination into a new set. Primitive forms use water as the medium; higher terrestrial or aerial forms have to rely on more complicated methods—genital organs and appropriate mating behavior, or floral parts designed to catch the eye of pollinators.

At the apparative stage, it is these secondary sexual manifestations which lend so much color to life and which so fascinate the naturalist. The peacock's fan is no more and no less sexual than the color of a flower, than the lover's longing for his beloved, or the swarming of insects. I say that all these manifestations are "sexual," but I hasten to add that we may characterize them in quite a different way, as well.

III.

The Inner World

Subjective Experience and Sense Impression

MANY biologists take the view that the study of the fine structure of living matter is *the* essential task of biology. Now, this view ignores one very important aspect of life—subjective experience. No amount of research along physical or chemical lines can ever give us a full picture of psychological, spiritual, or intellectual processes.

We are on very strange ground indeed when we first begin to look at psychological processes. Thus when we contrast superficial with deep experience, we are not thinking in terms of standards of length; when we talk of weighty or light-hearted decisions, we are not referring to weights and measures. Psychological studies, in short, take us into non-dimensional worlds, and hence it is not surprising that subjective experience used to be banished from scientific discussions. Within the last thirty years or so, however, there has been a radical change of heart.

Let us follow the new approach part of the way—to the sense organs—for only when we know what impressions from the external world can reach the mind, can we begin to form any idea of what the inner world may look like. The comparative study of sense organs has thrown a great deal of light not only on the great contrasts between the possible experience of different groups of animals but also on sense activities that were previously thought to elude scientific investigation altogether. For instance, we can say with certainty today that many higher animals can see colors, although we cannot, of course, say whether they register colors in precisely the same way as we do—whether their red, green, blue, and yellow are identical with our own. Bees respond to colors ranging from yellow to orange, and from blue to violet; unlike us, they can also distinguish a special mixture of yellow and violet—the so-called "bees' purple."[1] Moreover, bees and other insects can also "see" ultraviolet where we "see" complete darkness. Who can tell to what extent ultraviolet vision makes their world different from ours? To bees, poppies may not look red at all, and green plants, which reflect a considerable portion of ultraviolet light, probably look grey. As we probe deeper into the inner world of insects and study their highly developed eyes more fully, we are likely to discover many other peculiarities of their vision.

How great was the surprise when it was first shown that bees can respond to polarized sunlight, thus taking their bearings from the sun even when the sky is overcast! Since then, the same response has been detected in many lower animals.

We now know that birds too can take their bearings from the sun.[2] Thus starlings fly at a different angle to the sun at 10 A.M. than they do at, say, 3 P.M.—they have an "inner clock" of whose structure we know absolutely nothing. Who can tell in what mysterious way it ticks, particularly during long-distance migrations? Does the animal "know" what it is doing, or is directional flight an unconscious process? What do birds experience consciously? We can give no certain answer to any of these questions.

Yet—conscious or unconscious—it is a scientific fact that birds have a directional sense. The unknown mechanism which governs this sense is a link between the bird's inner and outer worlds, and hence an essential part of its life.

More surprising still was the discovery that some birds— warblers, for instance—can fly by the stars,[3] even when only a small chink of the night sky is visible. This we know because many nocturnal migrants make a sharp turn once they reach a certain geographical latitude, in the absence of any landmarks. Their exclusive directional reliance on the stars has also been proved by experiments in planetaria.

The fact that migratory birds can fly by the night sky strikes me as one of the most remarkable biological discoveries of recent times. It is puzzling enough that what are normally diurnal animals should adopt nocturnal habits during their migration; but how can we possibly explain their ability to fly by the night sky with which they are normally so unfamiliar? The mystery deepens further when we consider that this familiarity with the sky is inherited and not learned—for that is another thing that experiments have proved quite conclusively.

Incidentally, an "inner clock" is not the exclusive property of higher animals, for we know that even small crustaceans of the genus *Talitrus,* relatives of the familiar water-fleas, can take their bearings from the sun or the moon, though their brain has a diameter of less than 1 mm.![4] In other words, their directional sense is laid down at the macromolecular stage; it is guided by protoplasmic structures. To achieve the same effect artificially, we should have to build a computer of truly gigantic proportions.

Nature has many other surprises in store for us. It is now common knowledge that bats can fly in the dark by "sonar" —they send out ultrasonic waves through their mouth or nostrils and avoid obstacles by echosounding. This "sonar" system involves psychological mechanisms about which we can say nothing, but which we cannot ignore during discussions of the special world in which these flying mammals live.[5]

Another surprise came to light more recently, during studies of African mormyrids and American gymnotids. These—and possibly other fishes as well—can set up a weak electrical field in which the presence of any disturbing body is immediately detected. The fish can thus use electricity as a kind of third eye for "seeing" through muddy water. We do not know precisely how the disturbances are registered, though certain lateral-line organs are probably involved. Moreover, we cannot yet tell whether the fish sets up electrical impulses primarily as a means of avoiding enemies, of finding food, or of staking out territorial claims. I merely mention the electrical sense in order to emphasize the great variety of animal experience.[6]

There were times when scientists thought very poorly of the mind, and when man's predominant position in the animal kingdom was preserved only because the prevailing views of animal psychology were simpler still. Nowadays this picture has been changed completely.

The new approach to animal psychology was the result,

not so much of work on chimpanzees and other animals with an organization corresponding to our own, but of research with animals bearing little resemblance to us. Thus the directional sense of migratory birds and of bees has thrown a great deal of light not only on the complexity of animal behavior in general, but on innate behavior patterns in particular. Of course, as we go up the scale, we increasingly encounter instances of acquired habits. Thus birds and mammals can be taught to distinguish between groups of four, five, six and even seven objects at a glance, and to act accordingly. Though this cannot be called mathematical thinking in the real sense of the word, it is certainly evidence of a highly developed aptitude for abstraction.[7]

Like us, animals construct their inner world from sense data.[8] When Jacob von Uexküll first described the special world in which animals live and the peculiar way in which they experience reality, he stressed their narrow dependence on environmental factors. Since then, behavior research has made it increasingly clear that animals are much more "open" to experience than Uexküll originally believed, and that man's world is much more dependent on inherited characters.

So convincing have been the results of behavior research that few modern biologists would exclude "animal psychology" from natural science. The new discipline has particularly focused attention on those forms of behavior which were labeled "instinctive," and of which there seemed to be so many that the very term "instinct" became suspect.[9] The new approach is best illustrated by way of a concrete example: bird song.

It has been found that a warbler which has been reared in complete isolation nevertheless begins to sing quite normally when it is about two months old. Its song is "handed down" by hereditary structures. Not so with the chaffinch, which picks up its song during a short but impressionable phase of its life. As a result, chaffinches can be taught to sing like linnets, bullfinches, or canaries, and even with regional dialects.[10] What was taken for a simple instinct now appears as something much more complex—along with the purely "instinctive" forms of behavior there are others in which individual experience has first to be incorporated into the hereditary structure. As we delve further into the problem of behavior, we discover an increasing number of areas in the hereditary structure that are open to future experience, to future habit formation. However, this "openness" is limited—a parrot may learn to repeat words, but it can never learn to "speak."

Our own psyche, which remains forever receptive to new impressions, to new learning, and to new creative impulses, is "open" in a far wider, unique, sense. Thus while much of our thought can be copied and even surpassed by computers[11] no one will argue that computers are the full explanation of our own inner world.

What do we know about the "motives" of animal behavior? This question is phrased deliberately—in biology we speak of motives rather than causes, to stress that the world of living experience is not a world in which the language of physics and chemistry can be applied indiscriminately. All we can say about animal motives is that they reflect inner "moods." One of these is hunger; others include satiety, sexual longing, fatigue, and restlessness. A change of mood is responsible for the fact that carrion crows join together in large flocks during the winter, but form single pairs in early spring. We associate this particular change of mood with sex hormones.

But sex hormones produce quite the opposite effects in a close relative of the carrion crow: the rook. Here large breeding colonies are formed precisely in the spring. The hormones involved are identical in both species, so that the difference in mood must be a difference in the genetic structure of the central nervous system.

We call this type of genetic predisposition a reaction system, and the associated hormone secretion an action system. An identical action system may therefore trigger off a number of different reaction systems. Provided we do not forget that the two are closely related, we can, within narrow limits, isolate a number of causal links: a given stimulus triggers off a given hormone secretion, the secretion triggers off a further secretion, etc. However, we must remember that the causal chain as a whole has been laid down in the fertilized egg cell.

How does all this affect the mood? We cannot tell; we can only hazard a number of guesses and then hold them up to the mirror of reality. Mood—the very word makes biologists suspicious; so much so that many of them exclude it from any serious discussion of biological questions. They point out that the behavior of lower animals and plants, in particular, is based on fixed responses to light, gravity, touch, and chemical irritation. This type of response is called "tropism" or "taxis," words which suggest that lower organisms follow exact physical laws, when we know that they do nothing of the kind.

Many attempts have been made to subordinate biology to the exact sciences, to reduce life to a few so-called elementary functions: irritability and motion, metabolism, growth, reproduction, heredity, and mutation. All such attempts are quite fruitless, for they ignore a crucial aspect of life: self-activity and the independence of living forms. It was to counteract this approach that Wilhelm Roux, the founder of developmental physiology, suggested, almost fifty years ago, that all "elementary functions"—differentiation, preservation, etc.—be given the prefix "self," a prefix that characterizes the core of the whole problem of life.[12] True, not even Roux was able to say what this "self" really is, but he must nevertheless be given credit for having drawn attention to its significance. In fact, the term takes us to the very bounds of our language, which is designed to serve our conscious experience and action in everyday life, but is itself the work of an unknown entity, our own self. Hence it is not equipped to express that strange phenomenon, the self-activity of the living organism.

To Roux, that self-activity was centered in the organism's "inner world," a term which fell into disuse at a time when most biologists were concentrating all their efforts on physicochemical methods of investigation.

Why do I hark back to work which was undertaken more than half a century ago? Simply because Roux was one of the champions of a purely biological methodology, one whose opinions deserve a much better hearing than they have been given. The discovery, by psychoanalysis, of an unconscious inner world, has forced biologists, even if they do not use

Roux's words, to re-examine the whole subject of the inner world, of which the whole instinct problem is, after all, only a part. Thus the pupils of our eyes adapt themselves instantly and continuously to changing light conditions, and hundreds of inner processes function smoothly without any conscious effort on our part, simply because our inner world has vast resources and a vast "memory."

No one can localize the inner world, for though we appreciate the central importance of the brain, we know that the inner life as a whole involves the body as a whole. The brain is admittedly a central organ of experience, but how much it is itself governed by the body as a whole is best appreciated by a glance at the modest example of the *Planaria,* a genus of flatworm which is found in river gravel, and which has been the subject of many experiments. If we cut a planarian in half, we find that each part develops into a whole worm: the front acquires a new body, the back organizes itself a new head, complete with brain, eyes, and feelers.

Let us reflect on the enormity of the statement: "the back organizes itself a new head." What is this "self" which creates a new brain; a brain, what is more, whose function it is to guide the regenerated organism as a whole? It does us good, from time to time, to reflect deeply on such matters, not only because the process of regeneration helps to explain all those healing processes on which our own existence and well-being depend every day of our lives, but above all because it brings us face to face with the secret of the "self" which lies hidden in every single individual, in every separate creature.

Let us look at our own development. The human germ

which, at the start of its development, is barely a tenth of a millimeter does just what the worm has to do during regeneration: it too builds a brain with all the sense organs, and lays the basis for the emergence of a conscious ego. We are all agreed, that this ego is not itself the builder—the ego is a mere possibility of the "self." And who can say to what extent the conscious ego, in all its thought and action, is determined by its hidden mainsprings—in success and failure alike?

We have penetrated into two invisible zones—into the darkness which begins below the threshold of our optical instruments, and into the other darkness which hides our subjective experiences. The connection between the two can be illustrated with a simple example—color—for color can be considered as a purely physical phenomenon or as a purely subjective phenomenon.

Let us consider the physical aspect first. When I see blue, for instance, I may be looking at a pigment or a purely structural color.[13] The blue in a blossom, but also the blue in the pigment cell of a crustacean, is produced by a special substance, and any biochemist will be able to supply its correct formula. On the other hand, the blue in the feathers of a South American macaw is structural, *i.e.* it is produced by special light-reflecting structures. The physicist will help me to prove that the beautiful butterflies of the genus *Morpho,* which live in South America, produce their blue in a different manner from, say, the parrot and the jay, and in quite a different manner again from the colibri.

In studying the physical or chemical aspect of colors, we are solely concerned with the analysis of the structures or the chemical reactions involved. Things are quite different if we wish to examine the subjective role of color, the inner experience of color, that is. Thus, if we test a bee's response to, say, sugar water placed over a blue disc, it is quite immaterial whether we use structural, pigmentary or any other kind of blue; all that matters is that we test the bee's responses to a particular stimulus.

Living forms can be studied from many points of view, and it is essential that none is ignored and that no single one is prejudged to be more important or more "scientific" than any of the others. Only the sum total of all its methods can provide an overall view of a given generation's scientific outlook. The unity of natural science cannot be achieved by reducing biology to only those of its aspects that fit into physics and chemistry. Nature comprises every aspect of life—subjective experience no less than structure. Biologists ignore this fact at their peril.

The recent theory of communication, cybernetics, has made a particularly important contribution toward a redefinition of living processes. Cybernetics, far from reducing spiritual and psychological to mechanical functions, as is sometimes claimed, provides a clear view of what we have called the "inner world." For the fact that such biological phenomena as orientation in space and time, memory, learning, responsiveness, can be copied by a machine, shows not only to what extent our "inner world" can be grasped by technical means, but also how much wider it is than that of any man-made robot. Thus cybernetics brings us back to that mysterious "self" which organizes the equally mysterious ego.

While it is not our business to discuss whether information

is the essential link between "objects" and "subjects" which many cyberneticists think it is, there is no doubt that the new "science of communication" can be used to great advantage by all biologists who endeavor to study life in all its aspects.

IV.

Natural Form and Technical Shape

The Functional vs. *the Aesthetic Interpretation of Organic Forms*

WE SAW that, when Friedrich Miescher began to study cell nuclei, he had to use the Rhine salmon which was ready at hand, whereas those of us who study the laws governing macromolecular structures today can draw on the entire animal and plant kingdom. At one moment, we study an amphibian's germ, at another the germ of a bird—a fly's muscle, or that of the clam. Who, at the time when frog sections were the order of the day, would have believed that we would one day look to the coastal squid for one of our most sought-for nerve-muscle preparations?

Since molecular processes are the basis of all life, biologists in search of general laws can consult whatever organism they like. The lowest stage of life has its own laws—indeed, many laws holding at this, the macromolecular stage, are so universally valid that in the choice of material one can, if necessary, go to plants instead of animals, and vice versa. When it comes to the study of chromosomes, of sexuality, of heredity, and of metabolism, botanists and zoologists work together in exemplary harmony.

In this search for generally valid laws, the phrasing of a given problem determines the particular choice of living form on which to base a study. Thus we choose a given bird because its feathers "release" a given hormone; a given fish because the female "responds" to certain hormones by producing ovipositors; maize, vinegar-flies, or mushrooms because they provide particularly clear instances of genetic variation.

Now, this selection, which morphologists and geneticists are compelled to make in their study of forms and formal relationships, often causes them to neglect the whole for its parts. This tendency is unavoidable, but we must try to redress the balance whenever we can, and this is precisely what we shall now attempt to do.

All morphological studies take us straight to the question of structural relationships, and pose two quite distinct problems. The first concerns the resemblance between different types of animals—for instance, the fish-like form of such mammals as dolphins, or of many extinct reptiles. This resemblance is one of the great problems of evolution—for the time being, I shall say no more about it than that.

The second problem is posed by the fact that such formally distinct animals as whales and bats are both mammals, that penguins, which have flippers, are birds, that the slowworm is not a snake but a lizard.

It took centuries before these morphological relationships were explained to any extent, and before even the most unusual forms could be fitted into the general system. It was no accident that Charles Darwin devoted years of laborious studies to a small group of crustaceans, the cirripedes.[1] Some groups have been exhaustively explored—birds, lepidoptera, and beetles, for instance; others are still under investigation. Thus, in the case of squids, which have been my special concern for many years, a number of species have been described on the basis of only a single specimen; others, including the giant forms, are known exclusively from semidigested fragments spewn out by sperm whales during their death-struggle with harpooners.

The same disparities of knowledge appear in studies of extinct types which, after all, are a most important link in that vast relationship of forms which we try to reflect in our "natural system" of classification.

Every attempt to complete this system brings us face to face with a wealth of organic forms and poses the question of the relationships between them. Each attempt also provides a conditional answer. For centuries, the idea that all nature was created by a supreme force during one supreme act of creation was undisputed. During the past hundred years, however, the view has gained ground that existing relationships between different animals and plants are the result of a gradual process of transformation which, in the course of millions of years, constantly produced new forms of life by changing the hereditary matter of the old through a number of selective mechanisms. During the Darwin Centennial Year (1958–59), the claim was made that the mystery of evolution was now solved, in essence, and that the forces involved had been explained. I shall deal with this claim in a later chapter.

But before we turn to the "dark questions of becoming," as Alexander von Humboldt called the problem of the evolution of living forms, we must first look at some of the other paths that lead to an understanding of organic forms. Many of these paths have been extended into wide streets, into veritable highways, which run straight to their goal, and on which the traveler has no time to look at the scenery on either side.

One such road, especially wide and much frequented, is that which leads to the technical understanding of organisms. Along this road, we do not so much inquire about the structural plan itself, as about the efficiency of its various parts—in the present age of technology, this approach is not at all surprising.

In this approach, individual organs are looked upon as tools for performing special tasks in the service of the whole—the word organ, after all, means tool. Thus the heart is described as a blood pump, the limbs as levers, the wing as a kind of aero-foil, the fin as a propeller, and so on. School books are full of descriptions of this kind, and it is no wonder, since it is precisely this aspect of living forms that our technical mind grasps most readily. The fact that a leaf normally turns toward the light and opens out, but contracts its surface during a drought, or that a tropical leaf forms a kind of spout to let the water pour away—all this is perfectly clear to technical understanding, and is usually described at length in elementary textbooks.

Hepatoscopy or "liver inspection" illustrates quite a different approach. In this ancient technique, the liver was thought to have the task of predicting future events. Thus Babylonian clay models of a sheep's liver were inscribed with cuneiform signs indicating the "meaning" of every lobe (Fig. 6).

Because technical thought lies at the root of the current view of life, it is essential to stress its particularities. Many people

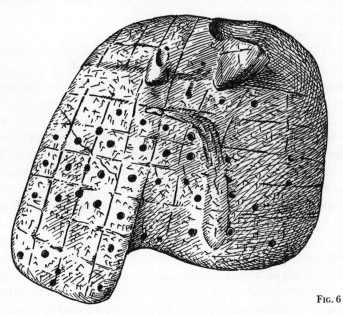

Fig. 6

The ancient Babylonians used the idea of natural sympathy to predict the future from the structure of the liver. The figure shows a clay liver used by Babylonian hepatoscopists. (1,900 B.C., British Museum.)

like to speak of nature as a great teacher, but nature teaches us in very strange ways, and by many detours. Take the case of bat sonar to which we have referred earlier. We know today that it is based on the emission of ultrasonic waves, yet we had to invent radar for ourselves before we could form any idea of nature's own radar system! In the eighteenth century, Spallanzani came within an ace of discovering nature's solution, but the final answer had to await the coming of the purely technical model.

Those who are familiar with the history of aviation know that the wings of birds were not used as models in early airplane construction. It is not enough to long for the freedom of birds, to worship winged Icarus—none of these dreams helped to make human flight a reality. A mere glance at the clumsy cages with which the first aviators rose into the air shows clearly to what small extent they consulted nature. It was only after a great deal of subsequent work with various aerofoils in wind tunnels that nature's own model was finally copied. I certainly have no reason to belittle the work of biologists, but it is important to understand the ways in which we think. Technical thought is a human characteristic, and only our own inventions enable us to grasp the true significance of nature's technical forms.

Similarly, recent developments in computer techniques have begun to throw a great deal of fresh light on the structure of the nerve centers. Thus it was not the structure of our brain that inspired the builders of electronic "brains." On the contrary, the development of technology has enabled man, as a kind of corollary, to explain many structures of the nervous system in terms of a technological invention. In particular, the invention of the thermostat has drawn our attention to the feed-back principle and has thus helped us form a technical idea of organic processes that were not previously understood.

The more strongly our lives come to depend on technical inventions, the more we become fascinated by technical explanations. Hence it is important to state that technical understanding can never provide more than a small glimpse of living reality, and that we commit a grave error if we overestimate the importance of that glimpse. That is the main reason why I keep insisting that we must follow many paths if we are to gain any kind of certainty about living processes.

So highly-prized was the technical interpretation of life at one time, that organic forms were held up as examples of technical perfection, as nature's lesson to men. "Form follows function" became the slogan of a new school of architecture,[2] which claimed it had rediscovered an ancient truth, a timeless law governing natural forms and man-made forms alike. The oversimplified formulation of popular Darwinism—selective preservation of advantageous forms; selective elimination of disadvantageous forms—has also done much to exaggerate the importance of those aspects of life that can be grasped in technical terms.

The resulting approach, which is so widespread today, has had devastating effects on our view of nature. For, after all, it leads to concentration on only one class of privileged forms and to the complete neglect of all others.

Animal patterns and colors, which we shall be discussing at greater length in subsequent chapters, may serve as instances of how the technical approach selects its objects. It fastens on only two aspects: the particularly glaring and that which makes the animal completely inconspicuous. An example of the former is the eye or ocellus found on the peacock's tail, on the peacock butterfly, and in so many other birds and insects. We consider all such glaring patterns special signals to animals gifted with vision: means of attracting a partner, frightening an enemy, or even of imitating the appearance of another, more formidable, species—for instance, a wasp. Inasmuch as we can understand them at all, we can also give a technical explanation of all those markings which make the animal inconspicuous and which we lump together as "protective coloration"—the white fur of the polar bear, the green skin of the lizard, the blue scales of certain fish, all help the animal to "dissolve" in its environment, to look as if it were part of its background. I do not have to go into detail, for all our museums and bestiaries are full of examples, precisely because they appeal so directly to our technical understanding. We call the striking forms "semantic" because their purpose is to act as signals; the inconspicuous forms "cryptic" because their purpose is to hide.

These extreme forms hold another attraction for the student: they are convincing instances of Darwinian selection effects. And, in fact, there is no reason why they should not be interpreted in that way—provided only we realize that the story does not end there.

Technical thought is often met in disguises which make its identification difficult, and which may lead to a great deal of confusion, particularly when the disguise is a scientific law, or a generally accepted scientific method. This is best illustrated by a concrete example.

Experiment shows that certain dental forms are invariably associated with other characters; in other words, that there is a correlation between different organic structures. As a result we can often use a single fossil tooth to reconstruct an animal that has long ago become extinct.

Now this law of correlation is, occasionally, taken to impermissible lengths—the established facts are used to support a speculative generalization, for instance the principle of natural economy or of natural compensation.

Thus the absence of teeth in the upper jaws of cornigerous animals is explained by the presence of horns or antlers, and conversely the presence of teeth in carnivores by the absence of antlers. Goethe made this "great law" the subject of a poem in 1820:

Siehst du also dem einen Geschöpf besonderen Vorzug
Irgend gegönnt, so frage nur gleich, wo leidet es etwa
Mangel anderswo, und suche mit forschendem Geiste.
Finden wirst du sogleich zu aller Bildung den Schlüssel.
Denn so hat kein Tier, dem sämtliche Zähne den obern
Kiefer umsäumen, ein Horn auf seiner Stirne getragen,
Und daher ist den Löwen gehörnt der ewigen Mutter
Ganz unmöglich zu bilden, und böte sie alle Gewalt auf;
Denn sie hat nicht Masse genug, die Reihen der Zähne
Völlig zu pflanzen und auch Geweih und Hörner zu treiben.

Whenever you find a beast with some special advantage, be sure you look diligently for a lack in it elsewhere. Then you will discover the key to all growth. For no animal whose upper jaw is filled with teeth has ever borne antlers on its head; hence our eternal mother cannot produce a lion with horns, try as she may; she lacks the mass to plant complete rows of teeth and to force up antlers and horns at the same time.

I have chosen this quotation deliberately, for we shall meet Goethe's scientific ideas again. It is easy to show, with many examples drawn from comparative studies, that Goethe's "key" is no key at all, and that the "masses" follow no law of natural economy—many mammals with a complete set of teeth have a surprisingly "uneconomic" nose and forehead.

But all we are concerned with for the moment is to show that this kind of interpretation goes far beyond the empirical evidence and that it introduces the kind of interpretation which we have described as technical. Moreover, the extrapolation of the law of correlation has a long history in comparative morphology.

We have seen that the attempt to explain living forms by technical thought focuses attention on some phenomena at the expense of others. In addition, our judgment of living forms is clouded by deep-rooted emotional prejudices—our minds take to some forms, and reject others. Gestalt psychology calls the former "good forms," and the latter "bad forms"; animal camouflage is based precisely on the fact that "bad forms" are rejected by the eye.[3]

We are particularly drawn to such regular shapes as circles, spheres, squares, and triangles. Thus it is no accident that in their studies of proportion, artists have paid so much heed to the horse, whose basic shape is a square.

Many art historians have argued that classical art came closer to discovering the laws of natural, and especially of living, forms than did any subsequent trends. In fact, classical artists merely selected those forms that are most deeply rooted in man, and critics then tried to justify this intuitive choice by turning it into an aim of nature. True beauty, Leon Battista Alberti said in the fifteenth century, is a state of perfection towards which nature strives in all her works. Heinrich Wölfflin, the great art historian, also believed that the vitalizing effect of classical art stemmed from its close relationship with nature[4]: "The artist's conception of beauty is identical with nature's." In contemplating the flight of the eagle or the heron, just as in the contemplation of classical works of art, "we enjoy the rare fortune of participating in a greater and purer existence. Moreover, they are right who hold that the formal concepts of classical art are at one with creative nature; the vitalizing effect of true classicism is explained by this very relationship."

By means of this constant and deliberate selection of pleasing phenomena, "nature" is turned into a kind of paradise. Where the biologist sees an impenetrable jungle, the art historian sees a carefully tended park.

The artists themselves have long ago redressed the balance, opposing the idyllic park of the classicists with the demoniacal wilderness of Hieronymus Bosch and others.

Thus it is no accident that the uninspired revival of Renaissance art in the late nineteenth century was ousted by trends that stressed the hidden beauty of absurd, cruel, and repellent forms. What had previously been relegated to the curiosity cabinet or the lumber room was now brought out into the open—the "noble" forms gave way to insects, spiders and krakens.

However, with the rise of modern technology, a new idea —that nature's aim is technical efficiency rather than perfection of form—has been gaining ground, so much so that, where Wölfflin spoke of the perfection and vitality of natural forms, van de Velde eulogises the natural beauty of early automobiles and of the first airplanes. And yet these early inventions now strike us as being fit for nothing but comic films!

The combination of intuitive preferences with technical thought leads to the selection of new forms: those that appeal to both at once. The stag, the gazelle, the greyhound, the horse, the eagle, the streamlined shape of a fish, the elegant motion of a snake—these are but a few forms that have a special fascination for modern man.

If we wish to gain any real understanding of living forms, we must become aware of this tendency. We must remember that our aesthetic prejudices and our technical thought constantly affect all our statements about animal and plant forms, and that, whereas many of our common judgments about "low vermin" and "noble beasts" reflect real hierarchical distinctions in the animal and plant kingdoms, others are dictated by current fashions.

Far from deriding all subjective judgments, the biologist must merely try to understand the restrictive role they may play in all attempts to understand nature. He must cease to ignore those forms which neither "strike" nor "deceive" our eyes, for between the conspicuous and the inconspicuous lies a far vaster range of "neutrals," of optically indifferent forms, and it is these which are the rule in many groups of animals. Moreover, in genetics we know that the neutral forms are the basis from which all the striking forms—semantic and cryptic alike—have arisen.

Those forms which appeal directly to our technical understanding bring us face to face with the problem of biological function. No one will deny the fruitfulness of functional analysis: physiological research is one of the major branches of biology, and morphology has been quickened into new life when it turned to functional morphology. But the appreciation of this fact must not make us forget where the limits of this new discipline lie.

A glance at the history of architecture may prove helpful in this respect. As a reaction against those who reveled in the glorious past, who turned post offices and banks into temples of antiquity, there arose a school of architects who proclaimed the gospel of functional building in which false façades and doric columns were strictly proscribed.

But carried to its extreme, the functional idea leads to the erection of efficient "dwelling machines" in which all but man's most basic needs are neglected. It soon became clear that the unity of form and function is no substitute for the demands of a full human life—that such "functions" as "entertainment," "comfort," "excitement," "peace," and "privacy" are aspects of human existence that no architect can afford to ignore.

Perhaps this is the right place to mention that behavioral research discovered the existence in animals also of an unsuspected wealth of "functions" relating to forms as well as to behavior. As a result, the concept of biological "functions" in general had to be considerably extended.[5]

But the problem of form and function is not solved by this extension. Even in the new conception, functions are fitted into a narrow reference system: the preservation of the life of both the individual and the species. The preservation of life is the only criterion by which we decide whether or not "comfort" is an important "function," or whether or not privacy is an essential "function" in the life of an individual. Only when they assure survival, do we say that form and function are "harmonious."

Some formulate the preservation of life as the meaning of form, and that is why our technical approach prefers to fasten on forms in which this connection is most obvious: on the torpedo form of a good swimmer, the strong wings of a good flyer, the camouflage of a butterfly, or the striking coat of the wasp. Thus we tend to forget the many types which lack any striking features but which nevertheless abound. We fail to appreciate that any real attempt to understand living forms must start with the "neutrals," and that those to which we pay most heed are, in fact, no more than extreme cases.

If we followed the correct course, we should quickly become convinced that there are many forms whose significance cannot be reduced to mere preservation functions, and that over and above those we have not yet grasped "functionally," there are a great many which will always elude all attempts at technical interpretation.

It thus becomes an urgent task to find a reference system which goes beyond mere preservation, and which accounts for all those formal characters that cannot be interpreted in technical terms.

V.

The Hierarchy of Living Forms

The Quantitative Determination of Sensibility

"IN NATURAL science, the progress from the lowest to the higher forms of life is termed differentiation and integration. By this we mean that distinct parts gradually separate out into contrasting forms, while becoming integral parts of the whole, that is parts the loss of any one of which leads to the mutilation of the whole. This is precisely the meaning of artistic development, as well—higher formal organization represents higher levels of existential force and existential abundance. . . . Every 'form' is life-enhancing."

With these remarks, Heinrich Wölfflin describes a problem which biologists meet in every aspect of their work—the problem of the hierarchy of living forms.[1] This problem concerns the botanist just as much as it concerns the zoologist: a flower represents a higher level of organization than does a moss or a fern. Moreover, hierarchical differences are found on the macromolecular scale as well, though here they can be neglected far more readily than at the stage we have called the "apparative," where hierarchical differences between members of a given phylum reflect evolutionary processes to the fullest extent.

The hierarchical problem crops up under so many guises,

that it is far too often taken for granted. Thus the systematist may not realize that he is solving hierarchical questions whenever he tries to produce some order among the wealth of forms he meets, or the experimental biologist may forget that in his choice of experimental animals he often injures a "lower" form in order to save a "higher" form of life. Every time we decide to wage war on vermin, viruses, bacteria, and protozoa, we make a hierarchical choice, and we do the same whenever we decide to save a given species from extinction—the Central African takes quite a different view of elephant protection than the European.

Though we think we are fairly clear about what we mean by "higher" and "lower" forms of life, we should be hard put to it if we were asked to give an exact definition. In fact, every hierarchical decision is an intuitive decision about levels of *sensibility, i.e.* about a given animal's aptness to be affected by external influences. Though sensibility itself is difficult to measure, it can usually be gauged by accompanying factors. One of these is the degree of relative autonomy. No one will deny that a migratory bird, which leaves Lapland, flies to South Africa, and returns to nest in the North, has a higher degree of autonomy than a snail, which is restricted to a small, moist strip of earth. It is generally agreed that warm-blooded animals, which can live normally under conditions of extreme cold, enjoy a higher degree of autonomy than newts, which have to spend the winter in a state of complete lethargy.

A relatively high degree of autonomy is also enjoyed by those fishes which can migrate from the ocean to rivers and then back again into salt water, or from the ocean to the beach. On the other hand, many squids, which appear to enjoy the freedom of the oceans, are in fact imprisoned in a very narrow temperature zone of ±5° C.

Autonomy depends on the ability to keep internal conditions constant. The more stable the blood—the composition of which depends on glandular secretions and on the intake or output of certain substances by the skin—the greater is the animal's degree of autonomy, *i.e.* its ability to live in different environments.

The ability to regulate body temperature is a particularly important stage on the road to autonomy. In the antarctic winter, when the temperature drops to —60° C and even less, emperor penguins hatch out their eggs while standing on the ice. The single egg is kept on the foot and is protected by a special stomach fold which provides a breeding temperature of roughly 36°–38° C. During the sixty-two to sixty-four days it takes the eggs to hatch out, the males—which alone look after them—lose about a quarter of their normal weight, which they regain once the females take over the task of rearing the chicks. Thus emperor penguins are particularly good examples of self-regulation under extreme conditions.

Let us look at some other aspects of this extreme form of existence: a high degree of autonomy always demands optimal feeding conditions. In other words, great autonomy always means great dependence—the spore of a bacillus is not subject to the same restrictions as the penguin. That is precisely why so many autonomous forms are found exclusively on polar shores, where the sea is a particularly plentiful larder.

It is hardly worth mentioning that the development of the

brain and the sense organs provides another criterion for judging hierarchical levels, and that the degree of physiological or morphological differentiation and integration provides a third. But none of the criteria we have mentioned so far supplies us with a certain guide—no single one can be used by itself. To take but a single example, though the toucan is restricted in its movements to a much smaller geographical area than most European birds, it has a greater degree of cephalization, and is therefore considered a "higher" animal.

Whenever we call an animal high or low, we step outside the framework of purely quantitative science. The hierarchical problem is, in fact, akin to the problem which historians or biographers have to solve whenever they try to assess human greatness, a greatness which cannot be measured in feet. Nevertheless, biologists, unlike historians, have a number of quantitative indications to go by.

One of these was introduced quite a long time ago: the determination of the relative mass of the central nervous system. Clearly, an animal with a central nervous system has greater sensibility than one which lacks one altogether. This is recognized even by those biologists who are otherwise sceptical about hierarchical questions.

Hierarchical comparisons must, for the time being, be restricted to groups of closely related animals since we still lack the means of drawing significant conclusion from comparisons between, say, an octopus and a crow or a rat. Thus we could compare birds, bony fish, or sharks among themselves, and the only reason why we shall concentrate on mammals is that their brains were the object of precise measurements by Cuvier as long ago as the beginning of the nineteenth century. One of the things Cuvier discovered was that simple brain- to body-weight comparisons do not lead to conclusions of great significance: mice and men alike have a brain- to body-weight ratio of about 1:49.

Physiologists then examined the role of the brain in the animal's heat economy. It took them quite some time to answer the question. At first they looked at the relationship between body surface and body weight, and found that small forms were the least economical with their heat: they have a relatively large body surface and hence lose more heat than the larger forms.

A comparison between related types then showed that increases in brain size with respect to increases in body size could be represented by an exponential function; in other words, if the logarithms of the brain weights and the body weights are plotted on a system of co-ordinates, the values fall on approximately straight lines. This was a great step towards clarification of the problem.

Among all those who studied the relationship between brain weight and body weight, no one has left a greater mark than E. Dubois, who is better known to the layman through his discovery of *Pithecanthropus,* or Java Man in about 1889.[2]

Dubois believed that the brain- to body-weight ratio is significant only if it is used in conjunction with a cephalization factor which varies from group to group. He therefore established the formula:

$$E = C \cdot S^r$$

where E is the weight of the brain, C the cephalization factor, S the body weight, and r an empirically determined constant which earlier theories gave as 0.66 or 2/3, but which Dubois himself evaluated at 0.56.

Ever since 1907, when Lapicque arrived at the same figure with birds, it has been generally assumed that all warm-blooded animals have the same constant r. On this assumption, we can calculate the cephalization factor C directly once we have measured the respective weights of brain and body.

Unfortunately, Dubois' calculations were based on an error: the assumption that r is a constant is incorrect.[3] In fact, r varies from one group of animals to the next: it is 0.58 in martens, 0.43 in squirrels, 0.33 in pigs, and 0.74 in lemurs. Similar differences were discovered in birds, where r varies from 0.43 (crested grebe) to 0.83 (sparrow). It was pure accident in the choice of their material that led Dubois and Lapicque to the same figure, and only when their work was extended to other groups was the error finally discovered. Now, if we can no longer use r as a constant, then we can also no longer use Dubois' formula to determine C. Yet C is used to this day—even for speculations about the brain of our ancestors!

My collaborators and I have followed a different path.[4] I cannot here go into all the details of our method of "intra-cerebral indices," and shall merely outline the principles we have used.

In the brain of warm-blooded animals, we select that part which may be considered representative of the elementary vegetative functions. Now, studies which have taken us from the colibri to the ostrich, from the shrew to the elephant or the whale, have shown that the part we require is a remnant of what anatomists call the brain stem. If we compare the weight of different "stem remnants," we find that it differs in animals of identical body weight. For instance, we find that the stem remnant weighs twice as much in guinea pigs as it does in hamsters, twice as much in stags as in boars. The stem remnants of three birds of equal average weight, but with different degrees of cerebralization—pheasant, crow, macaw—are in the ratio 1:1.8:2.5. In other words, the development of the brain stem is a measure of the general degree of evolution.

We were thus led to determine, for all body sizes, the smallest stem remnant corresponding to the lowest stage of evolution of mammals and birds. Using this value as our unit, we found, for instance, that the stem remnant of the tapir is 3.2, and that of the horse 6.8. We also found that the stem remnant of man is ten times as massive as that of a primitive mammal of equal body weight.

A comparison of the mass of the higher brain centers with that of lowest stem remnant of a given group of mammals of equal weight enables us to establish separate indices for the cerebrum, and even for the neopallium, that part of the brain occupied with impressions from senses other than the sense of smell, and from the olfactory bulb. A cerebellum index can be computed in the same way.

Table A, which was computed during 1945–1950, gives some of the indices of mammals. The figures cannot be compared directly with those obtained for birds, since these two great types of warm-blooded animals have brain structures that differ far too widely for that.

Brain indices must not be confused with intelligence quotients or school marks—they are relative and not absolute.

TABLE A

Neopallium index of mammals (after K. Wirz, 1950)

	under 2.5	2.5	5	10	15	20	30	40	50	over 50
Shrew	0.7									
Hedgehog	0.7									
Mole	1.1									
Bat	1.1									
Hamster	1.8									
Mouse, Rat	1.9									
Squirrel			5.2							
Porcupine			7.2							
Guinea Pig			7.0							
Rabbit		4.6								
Hare			5.1							
Armadillo		2.8								
Marten				13.2						
Dog					16.7					
Hyena					16.9					
Cat					18.4					
Bear						23.3				
Hyrax			8.5							
Elephant								70.0		
Tapir				12.6						
Horse							32.3			
Pig				14.1						
Camel						23.1				

TABLE A—*continued*

Stags:					
(Odocoileinae)	18.8				
(Cervinae)		28.2			
Giraffe		29.5			
Cervidae		20.1			
Lemurs	13.5				
New World Monkey					53.7
Long-tailed Monkey, Baboon			38.3		
Ape				49.0	
Man					170.0

Quite possibly such indices reflect the needs of the animal's heat economy or of other physiological mechanisms, in addition to providing a measure of all those cerebral structures which govern the animal's reactions to sense impressions, its "inner clock," its sense of direction, its volition, and its moods. In short, the index informs us about all those nervous processes which can be activated by hormones, and all those unconscious and conscious effects by which the animal can "relate" to its environment. What we call "intelligence" in everyday life is also reflected by the brain index, but we cannot yet say to what extent.

The index is a relative number, whose interpretation must differ from case to case. The cerebellum index, for instance, certainly informs us about quite other matters than does the neopallium index; the mesencephalon index of birds, which can differ widely from species to species, tells us quite particularly about the extent to which these animals, which rely so greatly on vision, assimilate optical impressions.

Even if we cannot relate brain indices to any single facet of the animal's total sensibility, they must nevertheless be considered fairly reliable guides in a realm where confused statements are the rule. We must look upon them as stepping stones and not as final truths.

Table B provides an illustration of the value of these stepping stones; it shows how the intracerebral indices of animals of like body weight can provide a measure of brain development.

TABLE B

Neopallium index of animals of like body weight but different level of organization (after Wirz, 1950)

Body weight ca. 1 kg.		*Body weight ca. 3 kg.*	
	Index		*Index*
Hedgehog	0.77	Armadillo	2.8
Muskrat	2.75	Marmot	4.3
Rabbit	4.60	Field Hare	5.1
Polecat	12.90	Cat	12.3
Mongoose (Lemur)	13.10	Macacus	32.4

Body weight ca. 50 kg.		*Body weight ca. 70 kg.*	
	Index		*Index*
Jaguar	19.1	Spotted Hyena	16.9
Sheep	21.3	Llama	21.7
Chimpanzee	49.0	Reindeer	24.0
		Man	170.0

A comparison of animals with distinct body weights but with similar types of organization leads to much the same conclusion:

TABLE C

Neopallium index of animals of like degree of organization but of different body weight (after Wirz, 1950)

	Body weight	Index
Shrew	17 g.	0.76
Hedgehog	928 g.	0.77
Leopard	53 kg.	18.3
Tiger	182 kg.	18.7
Antelope	29 kg.	17.8
Yak	250 kg.	19.5

The indices (9–13) of such primitive forms as the marten, hyrax, tapir, pig, and lemur (Table A) tell us something not only about the general level of differentiation in primitive mammals but also about characteristic differences between these species. Again, the differences between the index of tapirs and horses, or pigs and giraffes, reflect hierarchical differences that are borne out by many other investigations. The gap separating rats and mice from rodents of the guinea pig type —a rise from 1.8 to 7—points to generally neglected differences, corresponding, among others, to the evolution from an nidicolous to an nidifugous type of existence, and from a short to a long period of gestation.

What strikes me as particularly important is the very special position of man among even the primates (Table A). Man's index is an indication of how much vaster the quantitative jump from anthropoid ape to *Homo sapiens* was than even the great jump from lemur to ape.

The structure of the mammalian brain allows us—we have mentioned this fact before—to separate that part of the brain which is specially associated with the olfactory organ and hence to determine its mass. Since the olfactory bulb index is based on comparative measurements of the bulb and the stem remnant, it is quite independent of the neopallium index, so that a comparison between animals with a like neopallium index, but with different olfactory indices will enable us to say something about the relative importance of the olfactory sense. It is probably highly significant that stags and giraffes have an olfactory index of 2.3 and 1.6 respectively, and a neopallium index of 28.2 and 29.5 respectively. On the other hand, shrews and hedgehogs which also have very similar neopallium indices have a greatly divergent olfactory index (0.3 and 1.8 respectively). I add a few more figures to show the extent to which intracerebral indices corroborate other findings on sense performance and organization level.

Table D

Comparison of neopallium and olfactory bulb indices in carnivores (after Wirz, 1950)

	Neopallium Index	Olfactory bulb Index
Dog	16.7	1.78
Hyena	16.9	2.3
Cat	18.4	1.1
Bear	23.3	2.2

What we have done for mammals has also been done for birds, but not yet for fishes where such specific arrangements as lateral-line organs, electrical organs, and the distribution of taste organs over the entire skin, are associated with special nerve centers in the brain stem. Moreover, extant groups of fish are such vastly different products of evolution, that it seems impermissible to compare, say, the forebrain of a shark with that of a bony fish. Only by restricting our comparisons to groups with a related brain structure is the method of intra-cerebral indices any help in the determination of hierarchical levels.

Similar quantitative studies have also been made of the brains of insects and, in more recent times, intracerebral in-dices were used to explain many aspects of the nervous system of cuttlefish, the most highly developed group among the mollusks.[5]

Those of us who try to catch a glimpse of the secret of life at the macromolecular stage may occasionally turn our backs on hierarchical problems. And yet, even the biochemist cannot afford to overlook the fact that, in the final analysis, even the macromolecular processes with which he is so particularly concerned involve the evolution of lower into higher forms, and that, despite many important similarities, the protoplasms of the amoeba and the human germ represent a tremendous difference in constructive potential. There is no realm of biology in which hierarchical problems can be totally ignored.

We have been discussing recent attempts to express hier-archical distinctions in quantitative terms. It is time we re-turned to the phenomena in which these distinctions reveal themselves to our eyes.

VI.

The Realm of Images

1. *The Self-expression of Living Forms*

IT IS NOW forty years since I caught my first glimpse of the marvels of submarine life, off Heligoland. Forty years is a long time, and yet whenever I join my students and my collaborators in Villefranche or Banyuls to watch the miracle of transparent animals, I am still carried away by what I see.

The structure of many of these transparent animals—particularly of medusae, of ctenophora, but also of many marine worms and crustaceans—shows a remarkable correspondence between "inside" and "outside": the symmetrical structure of the transparent exterior reflects that of the opaque internal organs, which are often colored a bright red or yellow and occasionally a deep black. What is so remarkable in all this becomes clear when we compare the type of structure of transparent animals with that of higher forms, for instance of fishes, squids, or dolphins, all of which also live in the ocean, yet none of which reveal their inner structure. Our vision is arrested at the surface and the interior is hidden from sight. We see in the process of the development of the intestine, for instance, that the primitive intestine of the transparent animal is differently constructed than the more evolved intestine of the higher animal forms. The inner organs originate

66

according to the laws of bilateral symmetry that condition the external form, and only later, with the winding and bending and development of wrinkles, buds, and sprouts, is the original structure abandoned in favor of a tremendous increase in the size of the inner surfaces which regulate digestion, respiration, excretion, and secretion. Apart from the difference in the shape and position of their intestines, medusae and higher animals differ in yet another, equally important, respect: unlike medusae, higher animals have, not only an opaque covering, but one with patterns and colors which obey the law of external symmetry. This distinction seems so self-evident, that we tend to forget it completely.[1]

It might appear that the distinction is simply that between higher and lower forms. We need only look at the structure of salps, heteropods, or strombs, all highly organized but transparent animals requiring large internal surfaces for their metabolisms, and hence possessing asymmetrical organs, to realize that this is not so.

In transparent animals, the asymmetrical organs are usually packed together into a tight bundle which zoologists call the *nucleus vegetativus*. This bundle is the only asymmetrical part of an otherwise perfectly symmetrical and transparent body. Moreover, it is tucked away in a special opaque cover, which may be a glittering silver (in heteropods), golden brown or luminous blue (in salps), or, less commonly, deep black or completely inconspicuous. Other examples of this peculiar arrangement can be found in a number of transparent fishes whose intestines are wrapped in a conspicuous cover near the head, or in many gelatinous squids. However, there are other cases—for instance the rare *Phyllirhoe,* a marine snail—where all the inner organs obey the strict symmetry of the rest of the body.

Much has been written about the transparency of marine animals. On the whole, biologists explain it in terms of the high water content of the gelatinous tissue by which these animals are enabled to float. However, there is one aspect of the matter that is generally overlooked in all discussions of the subject, *viz.* why the asymmetry of the hidden organs should occur along with the bilateral symmetry of the transparent organs. While bilateral symmetry and the concentration of the asymmetrical matter at one point may help floating, such technical explanations cannot possibly tell us why certain organs should not only be concentrated but also be set off by special colors.

The morphologist sums it all up as follows: whenever metabolic processes lead to the sacrifice of symmetry in favor of surface increases, the enlarged organs are tucked away in opaque covers. Increasing levels of organization go hand in hand with the appearance of increasingly prominent non-transparent surfaces with special colors, patterns, and other dermal structures.

We meet the first rudiments of such structures in some medusae and, more strikingly, in sea anemones and marine worms; but to see them at their most striking we have to go to higher forms—echinoderms, arthropods, mollusks and vertebrates.

The clear distinction between "outer" and "inner" appearance at the higher level reflects a structural distinction: the symmetrical "outside" becomes the seat of many structures which, among others, are directed at the eye of a possible beholder, *i.e.* at a sense organ that can distinguish between "good" forms and "bad," while the "inside" becomes the seat of large-scale increases of the metabolic surfaces which cannot be associated with visual effects, not even when pigments appear in them. A comparison of the monotonously uniform livers of various species of antelopes or ducks, with the external appearance of the animals themselves, is a particularly striking illustration of the contrast between "inside" and "outside."

In higher forms the external structure obeys quite other laws than the internal structure, but in the simpler forms no distinction at all between "outer" and "inner" structure can be made. In other words, that distinction is a characteristic of higher forms of life.[2]

But what precisely do we mean by the terms "outer" and "inner"? Feathers are certainly part of the bird's integument, *i.e.* of its "outside." But if we examine an individual feather, it becomes clear at once that the feather itself has a distinct external and internal structure. While the lower surface of most feathers and even the upper surface of those which lie hidden beneath others have inconspicuous patterns if they have any pattern at all, the exposed surfaces are frequently constructed to catch the eye with special color-producing structures that can achieve a surprising degree of complexity.

For the moment, we shall refrain from discussing whether

or not these conspicuous structures serve a special purpose, for instance the preservation of the species. All we wish to stress here is that they are "eye-catchers."

The distinction between "outer" and "inner," or between "on" or "in" and "under" the skin, is only one aspect of a much larger distinction, for we saw that even the "outer" can be subdivided into the hidden and the prominent. Our original distinction must therefore be changed into: what is displayed to the eye is constructed differently from what is hidden from view.

This formulation brings us back to the problem of visual phenomena, a problem that impinges on all our discussions not only of living forms but also of living processes, and that runs through all philosophical discussions of the connection between sense perception and the external world.

To the biologist, the skin, with all its structures, is at first no more and no less than one organic structure and one phenomenon among many others. However, these structures are unique in that they make a quite special appeal to the sense organs of other living creatures.

The structure of the liver has no effect upon our senses, though soothsayers once thought otherwise; a musk gland, however, makes a very direct appeal to the olfactory organs. Again, the kidney makes no special appeal to the eye, but the ocelli of butterflies certainly do. The trachea has not the slightest connection with hearing, but the sounds which come from the larynges of birds are directed at an ear, and what is more, they belong to a creature that can hear itself and that can distinguish song from odd noises. The position of this vocal organ, deep inside the animal, is another reminder of how difficult is the detailed distinction between "outer" and "inner" phenomena. But that is a problem in itself.

Inner organs can assume "formal values" indirectly. Thus the dinner table has made us all so familiar with the kidney shape, that we use it in furniture design. But this is a secondary "formal value"; the organ from which it is derived is a hidden structure. Now, the "sense-appeal" of a hidden organ can also manifest itself more directly, for instance through its products. Urine is a case in point—it plays an important role in the social life of dogs, much as feces do in the social life of other animals.

We could use a technical analogy—but one that must not be stretched too far—and lump all these formal values together as "addressed phenomena," *i.e.* as messages sent by a transmitter to a specially tuned receiver.

Oddly enough, a whole host of phenomena can be explained in this way. Thus the front teeth, which are primarily organs of digestion, can be called "addressed phenomena" inasmuch as they may take the form of ornamental tusks, or have patches of bright color in the enamel. Again, the complex air sacs connected with the lungs of birds can often become a particularly conspicuous part of the bird's courting display (Fig. 7), and even the scrotum is occasionally transformed into an ornamental structure.

The contrast between structures that appeal directly to sense organs and those which cannot possibly be said to function in this way, is so important that we must emphasize it by introducing special terms for each. Accordingly, we shall call the former "direct" phenomena and the latter, which form the vast majority, "indirect" phenomena. The disdain with which physicists and chemists treat this distinction cannot be shared by biologists.

The difference between Goethe's and Newton's color theories rests mainly on the fact that Newton considered light and colors "indirect phenomena," whereas Goethe considered them addressed, *i.e.* "direct phenomena." We shall return to this point.

FIG. 7

Though most "sense-appealing" structures lie on the surface, inner structures, too, may participate in visual effects. Thus male frigate birds (*Fregata aquila*) can blow up their air sacs to indicate changes of "mood."

Biologists have already begun to pay special attention to direct phenomena in many fields. Thus behavior research, both in its physiological and its psychological (or ethological) aspects, is particularly concerned with the co-ordination of sense function with special "sense-appealing" organs. Similarly, geneticists are concerned with the preservation value of many direct phenomena. French biologists, in particular, have begun to distinguish conspicuous skin structures as *phaneres, i.e.* as purely visual phenomena.

Among direct phenomena we must also include those many structures to which biologists assign a "purely" taxonomical significance, and on which the description of species is so largely based. The greater appreciation of the importance of this taxonomical aspect is an important consequence of the most recent trends in biological research. Geneticists now recognize the role direct phenomena may play in selection and hence in the evolution of species; behaviorists appreciate the social significance of many previously misunderstood external structures; and morphologists go further still, as I shall attempt to show below.

Our distinction between direct and indirect phenomena may be compared to the psychological distinction between conscious and unconscious processes. This comparison gives a hint of the corresponding difficulties in our path, for it has taken a very long time before the psychological distinction was fully appreciated or, indeed, before it was applied to species whose organization differs so widely from our own that they used to be considered completely beyond the scope of psychology. Since then, behavior research—one of the most important developments in biology during the first half of this century—has opened up new paths to the hidden animal psyche, even in species where clear statements on conscious or unconscious motives are very difficult, or impossible, to make.

We have said that the distinction between the two kinds of phenomena we are considering is equally important—and equally difficult to make. Yet the difficulties must not prevent us from drawing attention to the facts, and hence from throwing some light on a sphere where only the crudest ideas prevail.

Our distinction leads us to a central problem of biological research: whether or not what we have called direct phenomena are laid down in the germ by the side of all those in which the phenomenal aspect is "incidental."

Every attempt to answer this question runs the danger of confusing our problem with quite a different one: that of the origin of the "phenomenal structures." Selection theory, with its emphasis on preservation values, looks for these values in every structure it investigates, and fruitful though this approach may be, it should, in every case, be preceded by a phenomenological study of the purely formal significance of the structure under review. Connected with this study, by the way, is the problem of the hierarchical order of vital phenomena, with which we shall be dealing in a later chapter.

We have just compared the distinction between direct and indirect phenomena with the distinction between conscious and unconscious psychological processes. This analogy strikes me as particularly promising. Part of an animal's psyche certainly serves conscious experience and hence "sensibility"; a much larger part, however, does not. We ourselves are fully alive only when our subconscious is working smoothly and effectively.

There are mental processes that are destined for consciousness, and others that are screened from consciousness, and it is the latter which psychoanalysts try to "analyse" in their therapy. Whether their intervention is justified by the results is a difficult question, which must nevertheless be posed if we consider the distinction between conscious and unconscious a fact of human "nature." The answer to this question seems to me all the more important in that, as we saw, there is a similarly clear distinction between two kinds of phenomenal existence.

I speak of a "clear" distinction, for that is what we find in the "optimal zones" of both of the realms we are considering: just as the conscious and unconscious share of the psyche can be clearly delimited in optimal cases, so also can the share of direct and indirect phenomena. Outside these optima, however, there lie shadowy regions into which our concepts no longer fit and for which, by the way, they were never intended. Every such region demands special treatment, and that involves an understanding of the clearer zones.

There is yet another aspect of the distinction between direct and indirect phenomena. Biology cannot ignore advances on other scientific fronts; if it did it would atrophy. Advances in physics have recently led into regions where indirect phenomena are predominant, where the main problem is to influence hidden molecular processes. In view of this emphasis on indirect phenomena by physics and chemistry, biologists, and particularly teachers of biology, have a special need to remember that those branches of their science—behavior research and morphology—which concentrate on direct phenomena, or rather on structures destined to become manifest, must not be neglected.

This brings us back to Goethe. We can now understand much better than many of his critics did, why he was so opposed to what he called the mutilation of phenomena.[3] It is a gross oversimplification to say that, because he expected the indirect phenomena to supply the key to them, Goethe was "merely" concerned with direct phenomena. Thus he considered the skeleton of a vertebrate a mysterious image of the living whole—which, in fact, it is to all those who are in any way familiar with organic forms. Now, the skeleton is a "hidden" structure—nothing in it has a direct phenomenal value or makes a direct appeal to the senses—and yet it is so essential a part of the motor apparatus, and hence of external behavior, that paleontologists can use the remains of, say, a skull to reconstruct extinct races of animals. With these remarks, I have merely indicated one aspect among many, of Goethe's morphological contribution.

Goethe remained a particularly keen explorer of all that is "destined to become manifest." Thus, in his studies of plants, he neglected the hidden roots in favor of the stem which alone rises up toward the light. The root is an indirect phenomenon; it appeals to no seeing eye, as the blossom does so impressively. Goethe's attention was focussed on visible processes—he stated it clearly enough himself. Now, this kind of selection of special topics is not a turning away from natural science; it is one of many possible paths that lead across a wide field.

We spoke of biological teaching. The distinction between direct and indirect phenomena is a natural fact which no good teacher ought to ignore; the importance of molecular processes must not make us forget that life as such is never fully explained in molecular terms. The following sections are written for the express purpose of elaborating this statement.

2. *The Interpretation of Animal Patterns*

At the beginning of this century, there appeared a zoological study,[4] which bore quite specifically on what we have called "direct phenomena." This little-known work, which earned its author, the Dutch entomologist J. T. Oudemans, the Czar Nicholas II prize at the 1901 International Zoological Congress, was devoted to the patterns and colors of butterfly wings in the attitude of rest.

We shall now examine two cases which illustrate Oudemans' findings. If we look at the small, pearly fritillary, *Argynnis lathonia,* we find that the upper side bears a reddish-brown and black pattern, while the underside, particularly of the hind wing, bears the pearly or silvery spots from which the name *Argynnis* is derived. Now, if we spread the wings out, we immediately notice that the extreme edge of the underside of the front wing has a pattern that fits in perfectly with that of the back wing—small ocelli, and a greyish-brown band studded with pearls. Yet the rest of the front wing is merely a paler imitation of the upper side: light brown with black markings (Fig. 8).

If we observe the butterfly in its natural habitat, the meaning of this peculiar arrangement becomes clear at once—only the underside is visible in the attitude of rest. Moreover, the front wing is so tucked under the hind wing that its reddish-brown and black pattern disappears completely. Here we are not so much concerned with the "form-dissolving" effect of this arrangement[5] as with the fact that each wing bears a

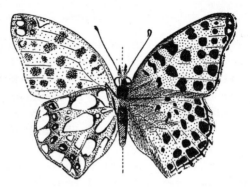

Fig. 8

The pearly butterfly (*Argynnis lathonia*) pinned up to show the right upper side and the left underside (top), and the natural attitude of rest (below), when only the pearly spots of the underside show (Oudemans' phenomenon).

partial pattern whose total effect is produced when, and only when, the wings are folded in the attitude of rest. This implies the existence of an inherited behavior complex which insures the combination of the two separate components into a visual whole.

If, instead, we look at the comma butterfly (*Polygonia c-album*), a relative of the peacock butterfly, we shall find that, though the upper surface is again vividly colored, the whole underside is particularly "cryptic"—small white commas on a dark background simulate the appearance of bark. This

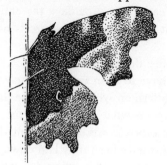

FIG. 9

While many butterflies push their wings together in the attitude of rest, the comma butterfly (*Polygonia c-album*) pushes them apart. (Another variant of Oudemans' phenomenon.)

cryptic coloration is associated with a characteristic form of behavior: instead of tucking its front wing away when at rest, the comma butterfly pushes it frontwards; instead of hiding part of the wing pattern, it exposes the entire underside—the underside as a whole becomes optically "effective" and dissolves the butterfly in its environment (Fig. 9).

In both cases, pattern and behavior have been subordinated to a total effect.

Let us look at the embryological processes involved. In the caterpillar, the four wings arise from four distinct groups of cells and remain rudimentary until the last larval and pupal stages. Every one of the four wings develops quite separately; not once is there a preliminary "test" to inform, say, the front wing how far it will eventually be hidden beneath the back wing. And yet invisible hands draw the required patterns on both wings at the caterpillar stage. We ourselves should have found it much easier to camouflage the entire underside and not a part of it only, but then nature is not like a modern factory.

Let us examine the whole subject once again. Four rudimentary wings have to form two completely different patterns —a semantic pattern on what will become the upper side, and a cryptic pattern on what will become the underside, of the folded wing. In other words, the pigment distribution of the mature wing must have been fully laid down in the germ. This is as true of many cases of warning coloration as of the protective coloration we have been discussing.

The co-ordinating factors involved are no less important to the animal than those which co-ordinate the muscles, the skeleton, and the nerves; no less important than all the many structures which assure "coaptation"—an important factor in evolution. The grooves in the armor of insects, into which the legs can be tucked away, are just another example of the same effect.

At the moment we are not concerned with the question whether or not a greater effort is required to lay down the eye or the heart than to lay down the wing pattern; all we wish to stress is that all these structures, no matter whether they assure vital or "purely" visual results, have their basis in the genetic framework.

In 1901, when Oudemans was the first to show the significance of the phenomena under discussion, he took an essential step forward, even though he himself used peculiar arguments to explain this step.

Let us look at his explanation. Oudemans realized clearly that he had hit upon a formal relationship—the formation of a co-ordinated pattern from two separate parts. "There is," he wrote, "an intimate connection between the effect of light and the appearance of the parts that are visible in the attitude of rest. . . . These (and only these) parts make up the exposed surface of the animal. Exposed to what? In the first instance, to the influence of light."

In other words, Oudemans likened the folded wings of the fritillary to a photographic plate, whose "exposed" parts can be "developed." The final result in the attitude of rest looks as if the two wings were exposed to light in such a way that the "exposed" surfaces are "developed" differently from the "unexposed" surfaces.

Since, however, at the decisive stage of wing and color formation, the parts which will later overlap are not "exposed," Oudemans' explanation is no explanation at all. That is one of the main reasons why his work has fallen into oblivion, even though it contained a large kernel of truth.

By taking their cue from physics, biologists have time and again been persuaded to apply physical concepts in a realm where they are quite inadequate—life cannot be reduced to a series of physical processes. Oudemans was no exception. He felt fully entitled to give a purely mechanical explanation of an effect that involves complex psychological processes.

Nevertheless, he deserves credit for having drawn attention to the problem in the first instance—thirty years after the first appearance of his paper, the phenomenon he studied is known quite generally as Oudemans' phenomenon.[6]

What was wrong with Oudemans' photographic explanation was that it ignored the role of the living eye at a time when that role was already being appreciated by early Darwinists. Their "explanation" in terms of selection effects was, however, no great improvement on Oudemans'. Let us see why. Such patterns as the zebra's stripes or the peacock's "eye" can, of course, be explained in terms of selection theory. We need not ask whether this interpretation is adequate; all we need to know for the moment is that it is rational, and that it enables us to relate a complex phenomenon to a vital process. It makes no difference whether a given pattern is considered a means of recognizing a particular species or of selecting a sexual partner, or whether it is cryptic or semantic; all that matters is that the persistence of the pattern, or even its transformation, can be explained in terms of mutation, selection, and isolation.

Yet when it comes to the origins of animal patterns, the selection hypothesis is not only inadequate but offers no explanation at all, for a pattern can only conceal or warn once it is there. Thus the origin of patterns poses a problem that is completely neglected by selection theory.

Selection theory is exclusively concerned with the preservation value of patterns. The patterns themselves are said to appear as secondary effects of essential ontogenetic processes, as the lasting witnesses of passing phases of development. The fact that the final pattern is semantic or cryptic is simply a consequence of selection effects favoring the one rather than the other.

How full of uncertainties and contradictions this type of explanation really is, is best appreciated from concrete examples.

The developmental stages of trout contain special chromatophores, or pigment cells, whose origins and development have been studied in detail. Among other things, it was found that the carotenoids, which impart the conspicuous yellow color to the ova of trout, are derived from the muscles of the mother fish. But why does the ovum need this substance? We know that carotene plays a part in visual purple, and this fact has suggested to biochemists that a survival mechanism may be involved. However, all those who have studied the phenomena at first hand have concluded that increases and decreases in the carotene content of the ova result in skin pigmentation—and nothing else. As the carotene content of the egg yolk decreases, so the carotene content of the skin chromatophores increases—the pigments of the ovum become typical skin pigments. No wonder that so many biologists are disappointed when they try to discover what "essential functions" the carotinoids serve.

In my view the problem would be much simpler if it were posed as follows: just as other organs are laid down in the ovum, so also must be the pigment system of the adult fish. It strikes me as most remarkable that biochemists should ignore this fact and that they should keep looking for what they call vital or essential functions, even where no such functions can ever be found.[7]

The same type of explanation is also offered for the coloration of shrimps—it is called a secondary adaptation, one that came about independently. For "independent" read "dependent on survival mechanisms that form an essential part of the metabolism of shrimps."[8] According to this view, the pigments of higher crustaceans are "substances which appear of necessity in the metabolism of crustaceans." It has even been suggested that the skin chromatophores act like phagocytes—that they absorb certain metabolic products to change them into pigments with the help of light.

Let us look at another example: in pierid butterflies, a group which includes the cabbage butterfly and the brimstone butterfly, we find a surprisingly large number of substances related to uric acid—in other words substances that are normally associated with excretion. A similar substance, guanine, produces the white spots on a spider's black coat, and the glittering white of many fishes. In short we meet this type of substance in insects, spiders and fishes, and also in Amphibia and reptiles. As a result, many biologists have come to assume that part of the excretory function—a vital metabolic function —is transferred from the Malpighian tubules to the skin, which therefore acts as a kind of dump for excretory products.[9] In this view, the actual skin pattern becomes a matter of pure chance, though it may later acquire a secondary selective value, and thus come to play an important role in the drama of life.

However, apart from guanines, the skin of pierid butterflies also contains melanines, which cannot possibly be considered excretory substances. In addition, there are scales which produce a variety of scintillating effects and which, again, have nothing to do with excretion. The more we consider the whole phenomenon of color and pattern, the more we are forced to adopt a quite different explanation: the colors on the wings of butterflies, the colors of spiders, etc., do not get there as the chance result of excretion, but, quite on the contrary, those substances which are important to the formation of colors are specially diverted into the skin instead of being excreted. I consider this "diversion" a part of the general structural plan which is laid down in the germ and not an accidental product of excretion.

It all depends on the approach. Either we look for survival mechanisms alone and restrict our search to the metabolic sphere, or else—and this is my own approach—we look upon patterns and colors as ontogenetically determined structures, and treat them as such.

How strangely the interpretation of patterns has influenced biological research in the last twenty or thirty years can be seen from another example, which is used in a great many textbooks simply because it fits in with the prevalent approach. I am thinking of certain basic patterns like the stripes of zebras or the spots of leopards, which occur not only in mammals but also in many birds, insects, fishes, and reptiles.

The existence of such common patterns suggests the existence of a common cause. Hence the patterns were said to be the secondary effects of "essential" processes, and all that remained to be done was to find these.

The results were first published in 1918.[10] It appeared that different phases in the development of the skin can be associated with alternating tensions and variations in pigment distribution. This is how the author of this theory, V. Haecker, put it himself:

We can sum up by saying that the primary patterns (spots, horizontal or vertical stripes) are secondary phenomena of the processes of skin division and growth . . . during which the formation and concentration of pigment cells occurs primarily and with particular intensity at the points and lines of maximum division.

This hypothesis fulfills all the demands that can be made of a general principle of explanation. In any case, the patterns are unavoidable consequences of the structure of the body, and need not, at first, play a useful role. Since even colors arise, as it were, merely as by-products of secretory processes and structural relationships, patterns are at first no more than visible expressions of the fact that all living structures are complex and that they grow. Spots and stripes, in particular, are simple "growth patterns."

Similar theories have appeared in great number—all of them open to the same objections. Thus all attempts to explain specific patterns in terms of specific phases of ontogenetic processes break down when it comes to the study of species that are closely related but differ in their patterns. In fact, Haecker's theory owes its success not so much to any direct evidence in its favor as to the general need for explanations of this type.

We have already suggested a different premise, namely that

the germ must contain not only the rudiments of the vital organs, but also the rudiments of all those structures which ensure the animal's external appearance. In technical terms, we might say that nature has expended as much energy on the coachwork of her living automobile as on the engine. Nowadays, when we ourselves have begun to feel a growing need for beauty, we are more willing to concede that nature, too, is concerned with ornamentation. This is certainly the view of many architects and other creative workers in many fields.

We do not want to carry this argument too far; suffice it to say that modern planners devote as much attention to "direct phenomena" as they do to the purely functional aspects of their constructions.

As long as our view of living organisms is dominated by the idea that survival structures alone are essential, we are necessarily forced to attribute the origin of all other structures to chance mutations. If, on the other hand, we grant phenomena a place of their own in the hierarchy of living characters, then we must also grant the germ a corresponding "store" of phenomenal structures, whose importance cannot be prejudged to be lesser than that of the others.

With this assumption we must renounce all attempts to offer a simple solution—those who have delved into the complexities of pattern formation have done so long ago.

The pattern problem is of particular interest to geneticists, for instance when they use experimental techniques to discover what elements ensure the emergence of certain butterfly markings.[11] In other words, geneticists are not satisfied with the explanation that patterns are mere by-products of essential processes, but consider them structures in their own right and with their own hereditary basis.

It was a significant contribution of Oudemans that he drew attention, more than fifty years ago, to the processes involved in the production of "direct phenomena." His explanations may have been superseded, but the processes themselves deserve more attention than is commonly paid to them.

3. *Snake Patterns*

The word "organism" conjures up the idea of organs, each performing a definite function. Hence it is no wonder that even the external appearance of animals is so often expected to fit into this scheme. Now, we have stressed more than once that biological "function" is almost invariably associated with preservation even though there are some functions that cannot be interpreted in this way.

I am concerned to show how large the number of these functions really is, and what role they play in the life of animals. Since a considerable part of my own and my students' biological work is devoted to just this problem, I shall use as my first illustration a subject that has occupied us a great deal during the past few years—the ornamental coloration of snakes.

We chose snakes because they provide a particularly clear example of rhythmical patterns across a very simple and uniform body. Geometrically speaking, the body of a snake is a rod whose contours are not "disturbed" in the way that those of all quadrupeds are—in quadrupeds the point of insertion of the limbs invariably transforms the skin pattern. Added to this is the fact that, systematically speaking, we consider snakes the descendants of quadrupeds of the lizard type, in other words, secondary forms of a basic type. Unlike lizards, however, snakes have a relatively insignificant tail.

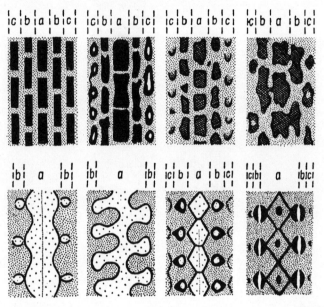

FIG. 10

Python markings. Top: development of pattern from the youthful to the adult stage in *Python molurus*. Bottom: pattern variation in *Python reticulatus;* a single specimen may have a number of these patterns in different regions of its body. (After Marianne von Harnack.)

Now for the pattern. Snakes (and tortoises) demonstrate the unusual case of animals with predominantly dorsal patterns

—in most scaly reptiles, and also in most mammals, the main patterns appear on the sides of the body. Figures 10 to 14 illustrate a variety of snake patterns, and even a quick glance

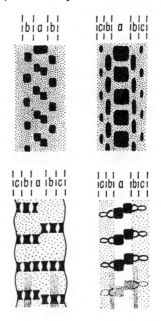

Fig. 11

Patterns of various species of the genus *Elaphe* showing shifts of originally parallel markings. (After Marianne von Harnack.)

at these enables us to decide whether or not the prevailing view, that patterns have no inherent significance but are merely deposits of pigments corresponding to the rhythmical segmentation of the inner organs, is correct. We know the general idea: the pattern itself is a reflection of "essential" functions.

In snakes, these essential functions are said to be the rhythmical arrangement of the organs of motion and above all of the segmental skin vessels related to these organs.[12] We have already criticized this kind of approach in general, so we need only add that in snakes, in particular, the true skin vessels form a network and follow a course different from the deeper vessels which are said to determine the rhythm.[13]

Moreover, the frequent occurrence of "displaced" series of spots and meandering patterns is further evidence against the "functional" view. The comparison of different snake patterns leaves no doubt that all these patterns have an inherent significance, and that the formation of each is governed by special laws of pattern transformation.

In the case of longitudinal patterns, we can distinguish three neighboring zones: a dorsal A-zone which often bears a double pattern together with a host of displaced and fused spots; a B-zone to the right and left of the A-zone; and a more ventral C-zone which is frequently missing.[14] These zones are particularly distinct in embryonic pythons, so that their subsequent development provides us with an excellent means of studying pattern transformations, and hence with a drastic illustration of the specific laws involved.

Only in two places are pattern changes affected by changes in the general body structure of snakes. The most prominent of these occurs at the base of the head; rarer but occasionally very comprehensive transformations mark the transition from the short tail to the long trunk. In addition, there are more gradual transformations along the uniform longitudinal axis, which once again demonstrates the specific significance of the patterns.

One of the most impressive illustrations of this specific significance is provided by coral snakes of the genus *Micrurus* and their relatives. These snakes, which are found in subtropical and tropical America, are most remarkable in that their final pattern, with its striking sequences of red, black, and yellow rings, is shared by adults and juveniles alike.

Those who wish to study the history of art must first learn something about those basic forms with which all discussions about epochs, style, changes of expression, and artistic mood must begin. Similarly, the student of biological forms must become familiar with basic biological patterns and colors. Now, the formal elements vary so much from one group of animals to the next that the zoologist, like the art historian, must generally restrict his observations to only a small sector.

In fact, the very pattern we have chosen as our starting point deviates from the typically longitudinal pattern of most snakes—even the most primitive *Micrurus* shows a tendency to black cross-striation: the typical black spots are traversed by stripes running from side to side across a red background. The subsequent transformation of the stripes leads to the formation of black bands across the entire back (Fig. 12).

As we go still further up the evolutionary scale, the bands have become regular rings, which finally spread out to such an extent that they become the new background: we now have black coral snakes with red rings. Incidentally, coral snakes representing various phases of these transformations are

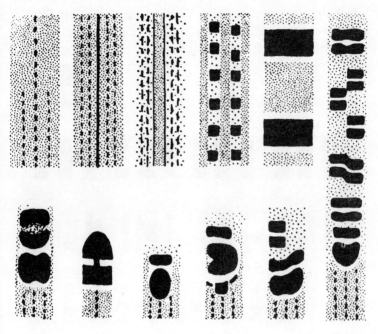

Fig. 12

Evolution of micrurus pattern. The diagram illustrates the possible transformation of an original pattern, consisting of two series of black dorsal spots on a red background, into a system of transverse stripes, which finally spreads out until the black becomes the background and the red the pattern (pattern reversal). (After Marianne von Harnack.)

distributed over a wide area—from Mexico, across Central America, right into Amazonia.

Let us look at yet another transformation of the micrurus

pattern. Even in the species we have been discussing, the black rings may occasionally have a yellow edge, resulting from a finer dispersion of the red pigment. The rings are thus set off more sharply still—experts speak of a disruptive contrast

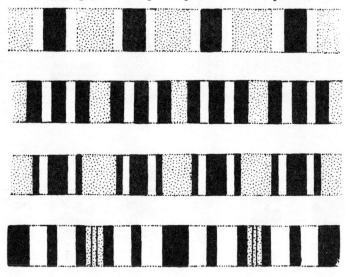

Evolution of iboboca pattern. The transverse stripes (Fig. 13) become edged with yellow, and the red fields with black. In the subsequent transformation, the yellow edges spread out, and the red disappears from alternate fields. The remaining, very narrow, red bands give rise to a new system of lines. (After Marianne von Harnack.)

effect. The further evolution of the pattern leads to greater isolation and intensification of the yellow ring. In addition, a new formal element is added—some of the red background scales become studded with black spots, particularly in the neighborhood of the yellow edge—and we obtain one of the many triple patterns by which we can distinguish between different species of *Micrurus*—every primary black ring is bordered by yellow rings which, in turn, are bordered by secondary black bands. We may call this the "Ibiboca style" of the micrurus pattern, after a striking Brazilian coral snake which is found as far south as $35°$ (Fig. 13).

But even this complex pattern is transformed further in many groups where every second red area is "swallowed up" through the absence of black margins. In this way, there is a marked shift in emphasis.

There are a great many other variants of the micrurus pattern, but we need not go into every one, since what concerns us chiefly is whether or not such patterns can be derived from the primitive series of longitudinal spots, and how they were eventually stabilized. Unfortunately, *Micrurus,* like the cobra, belongs to an extreme evolutionary line and we know of no species with a truly primitive pattern. As a result, *Micrurus* cannot supply the answer to our question.

For that answer we must go to the non-poisonous *Sibynophis,* a member of the Colubridae. Old World species of *Sibynophis* have a less striking, and hence more primitive, pattern of longitudinal spots or stripes than the two New World species: *Sibynophis venustissima* (Central America) which has a pattern of the micrurus type, *i.e.* transverse bands with yellow margins separated by red spaces; and the Mexican *Sibynophis annulatus* which represents an intermediate stage—longitudinal series of spots at the back, and transverse bands and an interference zone (Fig. 14) at the front. Four specimens in the Basle Museum have attracted our very special attention, because they illustrate changes in the interference zone with particular clarity, and because they indicate that even the

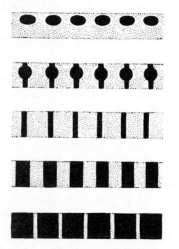

Fig. 14

Coloration in *Sibynophis*. Old World species have "ordinary" patterns (first three on top left) while American forms (which are often fitted into a special genus, *Scaphiodontophus*) wear the coat of coral snakes (fifth pattern from the left: *Scaphiodontophus annulatus,* Mexico). The lower series and the pattern on the extreme right show how some American forms combine both types of pattern, with the consequent appearance of interference zones. These double patterns may well represent a juvenile coat, which is missing in all poisonous coral snakes. (After Marianne von Harnack.)

extinct ancestors of *Micrurus* must have had "primary" patterns. But not even *Sibynophis* can provide the complete answer—like *Micrurus* it fails to tell us anything about the stabilization of all those changeable genetic structures which produce the different "styles" of snake pattern.

I cannot leave the problem of snake patterns without broaching the question why it is that, among the widespread Sibynophis group, only the two American species should have the yellow, red, and black pattern of the poisonous coral snakes. Now both types are found exclusively in America, so that many biologists consider the sibynophis pattern a specially clear instance of what Bates and Wallace have called "mimicry," *i.e.* the imitation by a harmless creature of the coat of a dangerous or distasteful model, which other species have learned to avoid.[15] But precisely because *Micrurus* is highly poisonous—a single bite may kill a man, let alone a smaller mammal or a bird—it cannot be called a mimetic model. After all, avoidance of a given model has to be learned by experience, and, in the case of *Micrurus,* no such experience can be gathered—its bite means immediate death.

The mimicry hypothesis fails in yet another important respect: the model must be very widespread—wasps are a case in point—if imitation is to serve any great purpose. In the case of *Micrurus* however, the alleged "imitators" outnumber the "models" by far. Hence when it comes to *Sibynophis,* we must reject the mimetic hypothesis altogether.

Nevertheless it remains a fact that only the two American species of *Sibynophis* have the striking pattern of *Micrurus.* Hence it might be argued that, even if no protective effects can be detected today, it is quite possible that they were present in the past. Thus, ancestors of *Micrurus* may well have been far less poisonous than their descendants, so that many of their victims may have survived and learned to shun the ominous pattern. Now, even if that were the case, the mimicry hypothesis would still fail to explain the origin of the pattern itself. After all, before there can be mimicry there has to be a model —the micrurus style is a prerequisite of mimicry, but is not explained by it. Similarly, the mimic must have the ability to copy a given model, otherwise he could not implement his "choice." The mimicry hypothesis can tell us something about the selective value of existing patterns, but nothing about pattern formation.

Genetics, too, can tell us little more than that variations in pattern correspond to variations in the total system of herediary processes which participate in the pattern. Now, that "correspondence" remains a great mystery—the mystery of the connection between macromolecular transformations and their consequences on the higher, apparative level.

Though it may take a very long time before the genesis of pattern variation is fully understood, this fact must not prevent us from making a careful analysis of the patterns themselves, for only in that way can we discover what precisely it is we expect the genetical analysis to explain.

The possible survival value of the micrurus pattern strikes me as being very small indeed, though a deeper study of the habits of these snakes may well cause me to alter my opinion. Among other things, that study may throw a great deal of light on the role of snake patterns in sexual attraction. But whatever the vital significance, it is invariably a consequence of the pattern, not its cause.

Any close examination of micrurus patterns will show that they obey laws quite independent of those governing the structure of the organs of motion. This is borne out quite clearly by the independent rhythm of the patterns (Fig. 13). In my view, such independence is clear evidence that purely formal structures play a very specific role in the life of animals—they serve the self-representation of the species, and must be counted among the highest characteristics of life. We shall have to return to this question later.

The more closely we look at those phenomenal aspects of life whose sole purpose it is to serve self-expression and not self-preservation, the more evident it becomes that those forms on which technical thought prefers to fasten are merely the most obvious. We begin to realize that the vast majority of living forms cannot be explained in terms of technical or preservation effects alone, but that they must be evaluated first and foremost in terms of self-expression.

Oudemans has drawn our attention to "addressed" phenomena—phenomena whose formal significance depends on the presence of a spectator. Thus the butterfly he studied, dissolved before its enemies' eyes because, in the attitude of rest, the formal elements of its wing patterns assumed the appearance of bark. No doubt, the micrurus pattern, too, with its striking coloration, must be included among the addressed optical phenomena, and yet there is a characteristic difference between the two. In the butterfly, a purely optical effect is ensured by the correspondence of posture, wing shape, and coloration. In *Micrurus,* on the other hand, any such correspondence is lacking. No one can say, *a priori,* that the stripes of coral snakes are "aimed" at a definite optical effect. Only experiment will be able to tell to what extent specific micrurus patterns are possible means of attracting a sexual partner, and thus "essential" preservation functions. It might very well be that that sexual attraction, or even the mimetic effects we have discussed, is based on the general combination of yellow, red, and black bands and not on their arrangement into specific patterns. Thus, whereas every least detail of the butterfly wing serves a total optical effect, the same is not necessarily true of the micrurus pattern.

How careful we must be before we associate a given function with a given pattern has been shown by experimental studies of the selective effect of colored patterns on a relative of the pearly *Argynnis lathonia*—the silver-washed fritillary, or *Argynnis paphia*. Both sexes have a golden brown coat with vivid black markings. Now, if a silver-washed fritillary, in search of a partner, is shown golden-brown models of different size it reacts differently. Again, if the golden-brown color is absent from the pattern, the male remains completely indifferent. In other words what the male responds to is background color and size—the rest of the pattern has no "functional" significance.[16]

And yet the pattern is there. This means that by the side of "addressed" phenomena there exist "unaddressed" phenomena, optical transmissions directed at no receiver.

In fact we are surrounded by unaddressed phenomena, directed neither at the eye of a sexual partner nor that of an enemy, phenomena whose sole purpose it is to express the phenomenal essence of an animal or plant. Leaves are a case in point—thousands of different forms perform the single task of transforming inorganic into organic matter. And yet, how much in the shape and the outlines of a leaf is not adaptation to the environment but pure self-representation! In fact, once we have begun to pay attention to unaddressed phenomena, we shall find them appearing in many places where, only a short while ago, we were convinced that we were looking at purely adaptive structures.

4. *Feathers*

The view I have been propounding has crystallized out during many years of familiarity with living forms, during which I have become increasingly convinced of the inherent importance of what I have called direct phenomena.

Since that view is based on the study of a number of apparently unrelated topics, I feel that the reader would benefit if I retraced my own steps. One starting point was the micrurus pattern; another was the plumage of birds, a subject to which my colleagues and I have been devoting quite special attention for many years.[17]

Now, the feather of a bird is one of the most complex of all skin structures. Feathers appear in so vast a variety of shapes and forms that they afford us an exceptionally incisive means of appreciating the wealth of detail that may go into the making of a single visual effect.

Let it be said from the start that the origins of this skin structure, too, are completely uncertain. This open admission, however, demands a slight qualification: most biologists are agreed that feathers first appeared in the reptilian ancestors of modern birds, and some biologists even claim that feathers are the transformed scales of reptiles. Others—and I think they represent the majority—hold that neither the fur of mammals nor the feathers of birds is derived from scales.

It is this kind of disagreement I refer to when I say that feathers have uncertain origins. Those who call their speculations on the subject certainties, merely obscure the real difficulties in the way of any positive evaluation of the prehistory of birds.

The oldest known bird, *Archaeopteryx,* a Jurassic fossil animal which was found in three valuable lithographic stones, already had highly developed flight feathers, and thus tells us nothing about the origins of these structures. We have to keep hoping that later finds may tell us more, but in the meantime we had best reserve judgment on the whole subject, and take the feathers as we find them—complex structures built up of horny epidermal tissue. Every feather consists of a shaft and a number of barbs bearing bilaterally arranged barbules. The barbules on the distal side of one barb overlap the barbules on the proximal side of the adjacent barb. Each distal barbule has a series of sharply curved hooks along its deeper edge, and each hook is firmly caught underneath the curling flange of one of the several proximal barbules which are overlapped by the distal barbule. As a result, the whole system of barbs and barbules is converted into a fairly rigid web or vexillum.

For a long time, feathers were thought to play no other role than to facilitate heat regulation and flight. However, we must now introduce a third role: self-expression, for there are many feathers whose external structure is predominantly ornamental.

This triple role of the feather must be kept in mind; if, in what follows, I concentrate on the purely phenomenal aspect, I do not wish to be misunderstood as saying that the other aspects are secondary. However, the other aspects have been described at such length, that we need not discuss them in any great detail.

The development of a feather is initiated by the formation of a papilla, which elongates and at the same time sinks further into the dermis. What later appears as a structural unit is the result of a process in time—every cross-section of a feather is a cross-section of time—and everyone who tries to look at a feather as a phenomenal structure must bear this fact in mind.

Take a feather with transverse stripes. This particular pattern is the permanent result of interrupted pigment deposits over only a few days. The "drop" pattern, on the other hand, is the permanent result of pigments deposited uniformly in a restricted area during the entire period of growth. We know many intermediate patterns based on various combinations of these two processes, and the shells of snails and mussels provide us with many instances of similar events.

We have to decide whether these processes are "purposive," *i.e.* whether they are directed toward the production of the final forms, or whether they are quite haphazard, producing the final result quite incidentally. In the first case, the hereditary structures of the germ must "aim" at the final pattern; in the second case they have no "aim" at all.

Much has been said about the validity of this kind of teleological approach. However, it is a fact that all organisms develop along paths that are laid down in the germ—and that is all we refer to when we speak of "aims" in this sphere.

What, then, is the place of feather patterns in the genetic framework? It has been argued that, since many undirected, chance mutations are known to lead to pattern changes, the latter must be purely accidental products. This fits in well with the prevalent view that such patterns have no more than a secondary selective significance. And, in fact, this view is not only possible but quite reasonable in a number of cases, particularly when the patterns are characteristically associated with the general symmetry of individual feathers—stripes, ripples, and pearly patterns are cases in point.

Things are quite different, however, in such cases as, for instance, the speculum on the wing of the wild duck. Here, twelve flight feathers and a corresponding group of wing coverts produce a total pattern that depends on the strict co-ordination of the individual patterns of all the component feathers. In other words, the speculum is the result of the same kind of co-ordination which, during the formation of the eye, leads to the harmonious combination of the parts formed respectively by the epidermis and the brain.

A particularly striking instance of this kind of co-ordination is the orange feather of the mandarin duck of China[18] (Fig. 15).

This feather, which is exceptionally beautiful, corresponds to the thirteenth flight feather of the common duck. The striking effect of this thirteenth feather is further increased by the special structure of shoulder and side feathers; in particular the shoulder feathers are lengthened to form a special border.

The pattern is therefore the result of the collaboration of three ontogenetically distinct regions. Another remarkable fact is that, of the series 13–16, only number 13 is fully elaborated, though all the others are potentially ornamental (Fig. 16).

The ornamental feather appears only on the coat which the mature drake wears from autumn to spring—in summer the male coat resembles the unassuming dress of the female. But, in either case, the thirteenth feather shows a slight deviation from the others.

FIG. 15

The mandarin duck of China (*Aix galericulata*) is a favorite subject of Oriental painters. The striking ornamental feather of the male (left) is the thirteenth flight feather.

What distinguishes the ornamental feather? Above all, the fact that the inner edge of the web is considerably broadened and almost orange in color, and that the shaft has been curved to an exceptional degree.

If we keep plucking the ornamental feather out, the drake will grow two or three new ones during a normal molting cycle. The replacement feathers show a gradual reduction of the ornamental pattern from December to May. As the ornamental feather is normally worn until the spring, the experiment has produced a variant which is not found in the ordinary life of the mandarin duck.

Now, the experiment shows that the greatest resistance to pattern reduction, *i.e.* the strongest tendency towards orna-

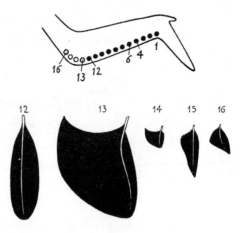

Fɪɢ. 16

Flight feathers 13–16 (see embryonic wing on top) are all potentially ornamental, though only No. 13 forms a truly ornamental feather. No. 12 lacks any ornamental potential.

mentation, is found in zones which are not covered by any other feathers, *i.e.* zones which lie in the field of vision.

In addition to this exceptional resistance to pattern reduction, the thirteenth feather has striking peculiarities in the structure of its finest elements, the barbules—iridescent lamellae are formed by the outermost pennulum cells, and long processes produce interrupted surfaces which reflect the light.

The special position of the barbules and their intensive zigzag formations add to the velvet effect. But all these optical phenomena only come into play once the web is spread out—this is the task of special anchoring structures, whose degree of specialization is at least equal to that of the flight structures. In other words, the formation of the visual phenomenon demands an effort that is at least as great as that demanded by a survival mechanism.

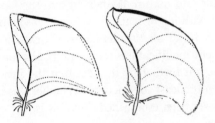

FIG. 17

The first juvenile feather of *Aix galericulata* lacks the marked shaft and barb curvature of the mature feather (right). It also has a much smaller iridescent edge. (After Anita Brinckmann, 1959.)

Yet another detail deserves notice: the first ornamental feather to appear on an immature drake is, in many respects, less striking than the corresponding feather of the older drake —for instance, the curvature of the shaft and of the barbules is far less pronounced (Fig. 17).

This bears out a general characteristic of all but flight feathers: [19] juvenile feathers invariably have a more loosely constructed web than their adult counterparts. Thus the earliest breast-feather of the blackbird has 36 barbs as compared with the 63 barbs of the later feather (corresponding figures in the head-feathers of a starling are 25 and 44 respectively). The looser structure goes hand in hand with a smaller "hooking area"—in the blackbird, the first feather has 11 interlocking barbs and the second 30; the corresponding figures in the starling are 8 and 24 respectively. Moreover, the juvenile feather has a smaller number of barbules than the mature feather, and some of the details of its fine structure are less pronounced. What is the significance of this distinction between juvenile and mature feathers? From the fact that young birds survive with looser feathers, we can reasonably infer that loose feathers fulfill all the demands of heat insulation, and that subsequent modifications serve purely phenomenal effects. This is borne out further by the fact that the juvenile feathers are very often the least conspicuous. Whether this is the general rule has not yet been established, but if it is, the consequences are enormous.

I cannot help being reminded of a comparable process: the transformation of leaf patterns in the course of one vegetative cycle. The simple basic forms are followed by forms with more complex profiles, until finally we arrive at the so-called "climax form." The profile of the leaf enables experts to assess the sugar content of a sugar beet—the leaf form is an indication of changes in the inner condition, and so is the fine structure and coloration of a feather. However, this does not mean that transformations in the appearance of a feather are a physiological consequence of, or a reaction to, internal changes, for these transformations are determined in the germ. The germinal reaction system built into the feather goes hand in hand with a germinal action system—both systems form an inseparable whole (Fig. 18).

The peacock's fan is one of nature's most impressive spectacles, and certainly one that affords an outstanding means of studying the special structures involved in producing visual effects. Hence it is most surprising that it was not until 1955 that a special paper was devoted to this important subject.[20] We shall look at the results of this paper at some length, be-

FIG. 18

Leaf sequence in *Delphinium*, showing transformations as we go up the stem, from simple forms (left) to climax form (center) and then back to simpler forms (right). (After O. Schüepp.)

cause once again, they lead us straight to the heart of the problem of "direct phenomena."

What the male peacock displays is not, as is commonly thought, the tail, but the tail coverts. Of the peculiar structure of the juvenile feathers in this region, I shall only mention one aspect: they are much shorter and tougher than the mature display feathers, and hence much closer to the structure of

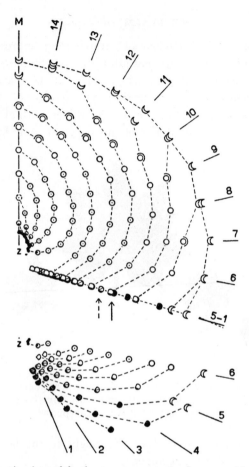

FIG. 19

Diagrammatic view of feather arrangement in the peacock's fan. Rows 1–14 form the longitudinal series; No. 15 forms the middle line (M); Nos. 1–5 form the inferior border. Circles indicate eye feathers; crescents represent edge feathers; fringe feathers are drawn in black. (After Esther Sager.)

ordinary feathers. This means that the ornamental feathers are governed by special laws of development—as they grow longer, they also grow looser. Thus all ornamental feathers have a strong shaft, but lack the downy part which normally provides thermal insulation. This role is taken over by special down structures in this region—one further provision that shows how complex a phenomenon the peacock's display really is (Figs. 19–22).

The "fan" pattern appears with the fourth molting cycle, *i.e.* during the peacock's third year of life. All the feathers which participate in it are so many variations on a single theme —the eye feather which shines forth in all its splendor on the central axis. In it, the finest feather elements, the barbules, are transformed into a single iridescent structure—unlike the ornamental duck feather in which only the tip of the barbule glitters. The eye pattern is built up by asymmetrical processes on either side of the central axis; towards the periphery of the fan, the eye feathers begin to thin out until eventually they have no barbs at all. The longest feathers, whose tips are farthest away from the central axis of the fan, have their barbs ending in a crescent—they no longer form complete ocelli. A different transformation appears in the extreme side feathers, which form a golden green horizontal base line in the fan. Here, the ocelli disappear almost completely, and the inner web becomes particularly loose, while the outer one turns into beautifully scintillating fringe. Now, it is this transformation which the paper we have mentioned calls the "most cunning construction" in the peacock's display.

In the center of the fan, too, the ocelli become stunted and

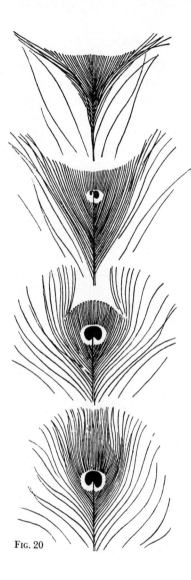

Transformation of a typical eye feather (below) into a peripheral crescent feather (top). (After Esther Sager.)

FIG. 20

the number of barbs is reduced. However, these central feathers are bunched close together so that the barbs form a copper-colored, iridescent surface with a black edge. The resulting "field" serves to set off the deep blue of the animal's neck during the display, and is an excellent illustration of the way in which different groups of feathers combine to form a total visual effect: not only does the field provide a striking background for the blue of the neck, it also has a form-dissolving effect: blue is a receding color while copper is an advancing color. As a result, the eye sees a concave optical surface.

This view may be criticized as transcending the scope of biology which, it is said, ought to concern itself with none but functional effects. I am not certain whether the limits of these functional effects have been fully drawn, or whether, in general, we can say enough about the significance of patterns to justify this kind of limitation. Hence I prefer to consider all optical effects and not only those which our inadequate criteria permit me to select. The formal peculiarity of the peacock's feathers is an optical fact, and hence its possible effects on the eye merit investigation.

Those who wish to discover the full significance of the peacock's spectacular display cannot, however, concentrate on its formal aspects alone—they must also study the general behavior with which the display is associated. After all, not only the peacock's feathers but also its behavior during the display are directed at an eye—in this case the eye of a hen.

Attempts to interpret the display in this sense have a long history. The first scientific study was included in Darwin's *The*

Descent of Man, and Selection in Relation to Sex (1871), and
Darwin's conclusion was not seriously challenged for many
decades: peacocks direct their display at hens which must,

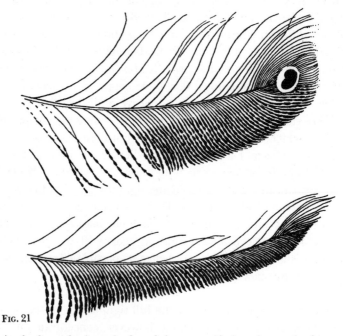

Fig. 21

At the lower horizontal edge of the peacock's fan, the eye feathers are
transformed into highly symmetrical structures, to form a scintillating
fringe of green. (After Esther Sager.)

therefore, be endowed with an aesthetic sense. It is their
aesthetic selection of suitable mates over millennia which has
produced the result which we so admire today.

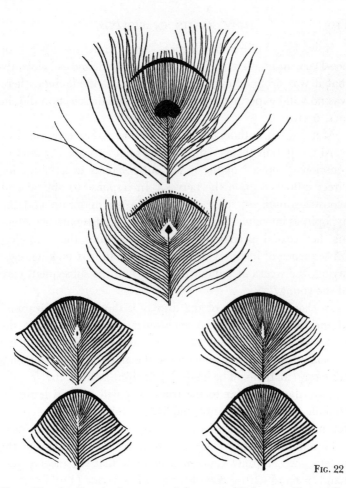

FIG. 22

The golden feathers in the center of the peacock's fan provide a striking background for the bird's blue neck. These small central feathers
become transformed into eye feathers toward the periphery. (After
Esther Sager.)

Now, long before the thirties—long before the apogee of neo-Darwinism, that is—this view was criticized so violently that it was dropped even by the Darwinists themselves; there was no valid experimental proof that aesthetic selection did, in fact, occur.

More recent authors on the subject have, therefore, put forward a different theory: the hen does not exercise any kind of conscious "choice" of the male, but responds to a "slow, indirect influence upon the nerves." In response to optical and acoustic stimuli, secretory processes in the midbrain and the hypophysis introduce hormones into her bloodstream, heightening her sexual preparedness and stimulating the "wonderful sequence of instincts which will result in nest-making, egg-laying, the weeks of patient brooding and the subsequent care of the young."[21]

In short, the object of the display is the "synchronization" of the two partners. This synchronization is prepared in the germs of both sexes, and affects not only the display but the associated circling movements of the male and the female's responses to them. The male keeps approaching the female, tipping the fan as far to the front as it will go, and letting it tremble with ecstasy, until, finally, she turns her back—ready for mating. The aim of the complete ritual has finally been achieved. In this quick survey, we have left out many of the details—we are only concerned to show that the display goes hand in hand with a complex type of behavior (Fig. 23).

The reaction of the hen was considered puzzling for a long time—her apparent indifference to the highly excited male was one of the reasons why Darwin's explanation was rejected.

Since then, behavior research has drawn attention to a new aspect of the mating display which throws fresh light on the subject.[22] It appears that the hen is not simply a disinterested

Fig. 23

The peacock's fan seen from the back. This view plays no less important a role in mating than the more spectacular front view. (After a photograph by H. R. Haefelfinger.)

spectator but an active participant in the display. In the presence of the courting cock, she begins to peck at her food with great intensity, and as she pecks at her food, the cock becomes visibly more excited—the two partners are actors in one and the same drama.

The full significance of this type of behavior is illustrated by other species of birds, for instance by the peacock pheasant (*Polyplectron*), where the cock himself presents the hen with food, or by the domestic cock and the common pheasant, where the male pecks at the food invitingly. The whole ritual is, in fact, a transformed type of chick feeding behavior—what was formerly a purely maternal or parental act has somehow become a part of mating behavior, in which the cock plays the mother, and the hen the chick.

In the resulting play, whose object it is to reproduce the species, albeit unbeknown to the participants, both partners have their proper entrances and their proper cues.

The fact that the peacock's ritual as a whole has behavioral as well as structural components poses the problem of the particular role of the latter. We have an important clue in the fact that the white peacock, which lacks the colorful effect of the peacock's "eye," is nevertheless preferred by many hens. In other words, the eye pattern is not needed for sexual attraction; it has a purely phenomenal significance.

We have been speaking only of the peacock—what is true of one bird is not necessarily true of others. Thus behavior research has found that many birds exercise a genuine choice of partner to form a lasting union. If, therefore, we have said that doubts about the female's aesthetic choice of a partner have grown in recent years, that is true of certain groups only, and not of all. We are only just beginning to understand the complexity of the problem and much research has still to be done, for even where we are certain that a choice of partners does exist, we know very little indeed about the elements on which it is based.

Thus the problem of "direct phenomena" leads us back to the problem of the inner world. Direct phenomena are, after all, more than means of communication—they are also the expression of the essence of creatures which, originating from macromolecular structures, have developed into beings capable of affecting the senses.

5. *Marine Snails*

The evolution of "direct phenomena" can follow many characteristic paths. Snakes provided us with examples of independent pattern changes over a long and uniform skin; birds illustrated transformations of one element of the epidermal structure. In many groups of animals, however, the transformation of external patterns is associated with a far more radical transformation of the entire body. We shall look at this type of transformation more closely in order to gain a preliminary idea of the scope of evolutionary processes as a whole.

The example I shall choose is a group of relatively unknown marine snails, not only because I have made a special study of them for a number of years, but also because I believe that they throw a great deal of light on essential morphological questions.

Let us first look at the characteristics of snails in general. There are many good reasons for assuming that the very early ancestors of our snails, which must have lived more than 500 million years ago, were the symmetrical creatures shown in Figure 24. Fossil remains tell us that the next stage was represented by snails whose mantle cavity was turned through 180°, though the detailed processes of the torsion are not yet known.

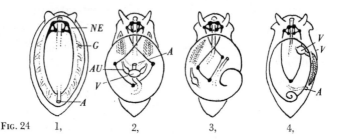

Fig. 24   1,   2,   3,   4,

The development of mollusks.

1) Primitive mollusks were completely symmetrical (five pairs of gills were also present in the recently discovered *Neopilina*).
2) The number of gills is reduced to only two, the intestines are twisted through 180° (torsion) so that the intestinal nerves become crossed (first prosobranchiate stage).
3) Further reduction of number of gills to one, corresponding to the presence of only a single auricle (second prosobranchiate stage).
4) The asymmetry of the gills and of the auricle is maintained, but torsion is cancelled (the shell spiral is not the result of torsion) (oldest opisthobranchiate stage).

A = anus; AU = auricle; G = gill; NE = nervous system; V = ventricle.

As a result of the torsion, the anus was shifted to the front, the nerve cords, which used to run straight from the brain to the intestine, became crossed, and the gills came to lie in front of the heart—the primitive snail had turned prosobranch.

It is most probable that from that stage onward, there began the development of those snails we shall now discuss: the Opisthobranchia. (We shall ignore the third group which includes our garden snails and slugs.)

In elementary textbooks, which have to make do with over-simplifications, we generally read that the Opisthobranchia are descended from the Prosobranchia, in other words, from a type whose intestines have been twisted through 180°. Some forms still show this prosobranchiate characteristic very clearly; in others, the torsion has been reversed to a greater or lesser extent—biologists call it detorsion. In the elementary view, therefore, those Opisthobranchia are called the oldest whose nerve cords show torsion effects and which carry a proper shell.

Fossil experts can tell us very little about the Opisthobranchia, since many species lack a shell and could therefore leave no fossil evidence of their existence. No wonder that the few biologists who know this group become the more chary of statements about the origin and the evolution of Opisthobranchia the more they look into the subject. Whether the origins of these snails go back to the Paleozoic, the Triassic, or later still, are questions which few experts would care to pronounce upon with certainty.

The whole subject of the structure of the original mollusk was opened up again in 1952, when a Danish deep-sea expedition fished up specimens of *Neopilina galatheae Lemche* from the Pacific, and identified them as representatives of a new group of mollusks with fossil relatives.[23]

The future may well tell us a great deal more about the oldest mollusks, about the origin of torsion, and hence about snails

in general, but meanwhile the biologist must base all his conclusions on comparative studies of what opisthobranchiate material he has on hand. Only the results of comparative studies
can tell him whether or not the simplifications of elementary
textbooks are didactically justifiable, or whether they are based
on so many idle speculations.

A comparison of extant Opisthobranchia suggests that three
events, at least, must have played a decisive role in the evolution of the group: 1) reduction of the shell; 2) concentration
of the nerve centers; and 3) displacement of the organs of the
mantle cavity.[24] We assume that all three occurred during at
least 250 million years and probably longer.

The size of the shell is reduced in many independent lines
of evolution; whereas the larval shell invariably retains the
coiled form, if only by way of a tiny spiral, that spiral is often
no more than a marginal vestige in the adult shell, so much
so that it has to be covered by two mantle folds (in some cases
of extreme reduction, even the last vestiges of the shell have
disappeared completely).

Shell reduction goes hand in hand with a more positive
process: the emergence of a new dorsal surface. The delicate
skin which, in the ancestral forms, lay hidden beneath the
hard shell, now forms a "dorsal shield" (the *notum*), and this
shield becomes a new center of transformations, whose subsequent course makes opisthobranchiate evolution a particularly exciting chapter of morphology (Fig. 25).

The second event that, as we said, played a decisive role in
the evolution of marine snails—the concentration of the nerv-

ous system—also went hand in hand with the reduction of the shell. We have many good reasons for considering those forms which resemble the shell-covered Prosobranchia as particularly original Opisthobranchia. As such they can tell us a great deal about the primitive nervous system: the intestinal nerve centers are spread throughout the body, and are joined to one another and to the cerebral ganglia by long cords which cross over as a result of torsion, so much so that it is often difficult to tell whether a given specimen is, in fact, an opisthobranch. In

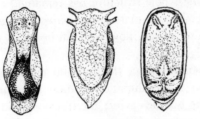

Fig. 25

Transformation of opisthobranchia: The shell is still visible in primitive forms (*Haminoea;* left), but not in subsequent stages, where the notum becomes more prominent, while the gills remain asymmetrical (*Pleurobranchia;* center). In the final stage (*Doris;* right), however, the original gill is replaced by an entirely new and fully symmetrical structure.

many of these primitive forms, even the cerebral nerve centers are at some considerable distance from one another.

However, with shell reduction there ensues a considerable transformation of the nerve centers: the intestinal centers move up by characteristic stages toward the head; the torsion of the gut, which is marked in the more primitive forms, ceases to affect the nerve centers even in the earliest stages of their migration to the head, with the result that the intestinal nerves no longer cross over. This, by the way, is also true of land snails.

However, the transformation of the nervous system goes much further still. Whereas even the cerebral ganglia of primitive forms were clearly separated, they now congregate on either side of the intestine. As they migrate to the top and to the front, they form two symmetrical masses which are joined to each other by broad loops beneath the intestine, thus demonstrating that the whole structure has remained a "gullet." In extreme cases, the two masses fuse across the intestine into a compact "brain" which, however, still bears all the sub-intestinal loops (Fig. 26).

Far more striking than this internal reconstruction of the nervous system, is the alteration of those structures that originally lay in the mantle cavity: the transformation of the gills, and the displacement of the anus and of the apertures of the kidneys and sexual organs. For once the shell has disappeared, the mantle cavity disappears as well. Organs that used to be packed together now become more independent so that each can follow those special rules of evolution which we can recognize in the final result, without being able to understand their causes. The gills may disappear completely, the anal aperture separates from the kidney aperture and the genital openings are modified in a special way. The Opisthobranchia are hermaphrodites with very complicated sexual organs— whereas the male and female openings are distinct in primitive representatives, they may be combined together in more highly evolved species.

One consequence of all these internal changes is the radical transformation of the external appearance of snails. With the reduction of the shell, areas of skin are laid bare that were formerly hidden from sight. These areas obey a number of special formation laws, all tending towards strict external symmetry, from which only the sexual organs are exempt.

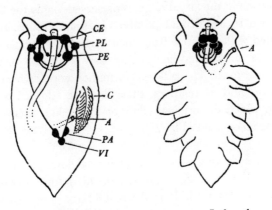

Fig. 26

Evolution of opisthobranchiate nervous system. Left: the scattered ganglia of primitive forms; right: concentration of the ganglia across the "gullet" of more advanced forms. A = anus; CE = cerebral ganglia; G = gill; PA = parietal ganglion; PE = pedal ganglion; PL = pleural ganglion; VI = visceral ganglion.

The resulting transformations once again emphasize the great contrast between the respective morphological rules governing the external appearance and the structure of the internal organs. While the internal organs continue to be subject to the torsion of the larval intestine, with the result that they show asymmetrical convolutions, loop formation, gland pro-liferation, and maximum surface increases—in short, maxi-mum utilization of the available space—torsion is cancelled on the outside.

In many species, the anus is displaced toward the mid-line and forward toward the head, in others it migrates toward the posterior end. In both cases, however, the intestinal loop set up by torsion in the larval stage, is preserved—only the hindgut is modified in length and position. In some groups, the gills are shifted with the anus from their original right lateral posi-tion to the dorsal mid-line, where they assume a bilaterally symmetrical form. This gill transformation goes so far that, in *Archidorus* and its relatives, the gills have adopted a flower shape in which the original comb or featherlike organ can no longer be recognized (Fig. 25).

The most striking expression of formal laws governing the external structure is the emergence of the notum, to which we have already referred. It is the seat of the most varied epi-dermal formations: processes and patterns of all kinds are combined into that profusion of forms which makes the ob-servation of marine snails such a constant source of delight (Figs. 27–28).

These processes may be recurring projections along the edges of the notum, or else they may be shaped like wings which fold back over the dorsal surface. The lateral processes often produce highly complicated ornamental structures: hand-shaped lobes, ramified branches, and conical or flattened amphorae.

In a number of groups, the notum bears transverse rows of long tubes which communicate with the largest of the intestinal glands, thus helping to increase the digestive surface. In the aeolids, which feed on polyps, the tips of these dorsal tubes

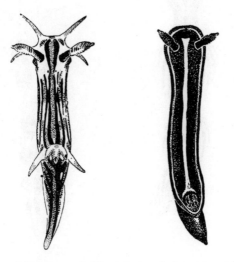

Fig. 27

Polycera quadrilineata and *Glossodoris tricolor,* two striking species found in every ocean. Their coloration is one of many possible variations on a central theme, and makes them one of nature's most fascinating spectacles.

Polycera quadrilineata is orange and black; *Glossodoris tricolor* is ultramarine with a white stripe in the center and a yellow stripe near the periphery.

contain a special pocket for collecting and excreting nettle cells, whose presence poses very special problems to biologists.[25] At one time, it was seriously suggested that the nettle cells were

Fig. 28

Two aeolids represent extreme forms of opisthobranchiate development. Left: *Facelina rubrovittata* with red dorsal stripes; right: *Trinchesia coerulea,* whose spadix is a beautiful mixture of ultramarine,
gold, and black. The spadices of aeolids are studded with nettle organs.

produced by the snail itself, but since then it has become quite
clear that they are ingested.

Because nettle cells are the only means of defense of polyps
and medusae, it seemed reasonable to assume that aeolids, too,
used them as weapons. More recently, however, a new in-

terpretation has been put forward: aeolids swallow their nettle cells together with polyps, and, since they cannot digest them, they have to store them up and to evacuate them from time to time. The romantic idea of hidden weapons has, therefore, given way to the more prosaic idea of a well-organized system of evacuation.

A whole chapter could be written on the colors which appear in the notum, though little is known about their chemical structure. The entire spectral range is represented, from pure red to violet, as well as a variety of mixtures.[26] Apart from pigments, there are a host of structural colors—white, for instance—and also many shades of blue.

It is now forty years since my studies of marine life first took me to Heligoland and to Brittany. I was carried away by their beauty from the moment I spotted my first *Doto coronata*, and my first *Aegirus* with its radiant blue points on a brown velvet cushion. My later acquaintance with Mediterranean forms only served to increase the spell, and the fact that, year after year, I am able to introduce young zoologists to these marvels is one of the greatest joys I know.

The black and white drawings in this book cannot convey more than a very vague impression of one of nature's most colorful spectacles.

We have chosen the Opisthobranchia as one example among many to illustrate nature's profusion of colorful forms. If I have concentrated on their external appearance, it is not because I consider the structure and the function of the inner organs unimportant, but simply because the latter can be

investigated by the tried and tested methods of biological research, whereas the former cannot.

True, some purely formal aspects, too, can be explained in
functional terms—for instance, the placing of the large tenta-
cles at the front, or the presence of mucus glands and cilia in
the "foot" which has to provide a constant carpet of mucus.
However, the particular placing of the gills, for instance, cannot be explained in this way, since the gills would function
equally well in another position. The fact, moreover, that one
group has feather-shaped gills on the right side, a second
flower-shaped gills on the back, and a third no gills at all,
eludes all purely functional interpretations.

We saw that the external symmetry of late opisthobranchia
hides a marked internal asymmetry due to torsion. Thus the
torsion problem lies at the very heart of all attempts to explain
the peculiar shape of mollusks.

Torsion is usually attributed to two causes: either to hitherto
unexplained transformation laws or else to the repeated selection of beneficial mutations.

Most biologists consider the second view, if not absolutely
certain, then at least the more probable of the two. However,
this view comes up against a central difficulty: the most crucial
stages in the evolution of mollusks, during which torsion was
"selected," lie back 500 million years. In other words, whereas
we can actually watch certain selection effects at work—for
instance the positive selection of dark varieties of butterfly in
industrial smog—the "selective" interpretation of torsion, *i.e.*
of an event that cannot be repeated experimentally, is no more
than speculation. This does not necessarily invalidate the in-

terpretation, but does suggest that it must be treated with great circumspection.

There are a great many theories about the origins of mollusks, but most start from the assumption that the oldest mollusks had posterior mantle cavities and that those forms fared best whose mantle was gradually shifted to the front—in the new position, the heart and gills are less compressed and hence less functionally impeded when the animal has to withdraw into its shell.

From this type of interpretation, however, we learn nothing about the actual process of transformation, since, quite obviously, selection can only favor the final result, and not a host of intermediate stages. That is the reason why many biologists have begun to accept the idea of relatively fast evolutionary processes, which is borne out by the discovery that Cambrian strata contain mollusks of the symmetrical, ancestral, type, side by side with mollusks in which torsion has been realized. However, this tells us little about the actual time interval separating the two, though it may explain the absence of intermediate stages.

During the past twenty years or so, the subject of torsion has also been considered by embryologists, whose studies have shed a great deal of fresh light on the subject. After all, torsion is not only a prehistoric fact, but a process that is being repeated here and now, year after year, in the development of every young mollusk.

The earliest embryonic processes in the fertilized germ cells of snails and mussels are highly symmetrical. Primitive forms, e.g. the coastal limpet (*Patella*) or the sea ear (*Haliotis*), even have symmetrical larvae—the so-called trochophores.

At the larval stage, there starts a series of obligatory genetic processes which, in a short time—in individual species in a few minutes—produces torsion step by step.[27] We cannot describe these processes here—suffice it to say that they have been carefully studied and that they are well-known. Among others, the new position of the mantle cavity enables the larva to withdraw its "sail" and head into a much more favorable position than before.

These and similar embryological discoveries have drawn the attention of many morphologists to the work of W. Garstang, who, as early as 1928, suggested that sudden mutations during embryonic development can, if they are associated with additional mutations, lead to the permanent fixation of the mature form—"maturation at the juvenile stage" is what many experts call it.[28] In mollusks, at any rate, we know of no transitional stage between original symmetry (posterior mantle cavity) and torsion (anterior mantle cavity). Embryological observations suggest that even adult transformation in the distant past could have been based on the "all or nothing" principle.

However, the whole approach is open to a great many objections. First of all, the identification of the fixation of embryonic and larval forms with characteristics of the mature forms is a hypothesis that has never been proved, and that leads to many fresh difficulties. Secondly, the processes we observe in free-living larvae are based on the complicated combination of a host of embryonic processes into a harmonious whole, which no experimentally demonstrable mutation effects could reproduce. These larval processes are the result of the co-ordination of hereditary structures that are just as much directed at full torsion as other structures are directed at, say, full cerebral or visceral development.

The fact that, in some species, full torsion is realized within a few minutes, shows merely that torsion is built into the germ as a short-term process. It tells us nothing at all about the historical origin of the organization in which these processes culminate.

The theory of evolution has seized upon the idea of "maturation at the juvenile stage," because it seems to provide a possible explanation of the problem of cladogenesis, *i.e.* the origin of new types and races, or at least to bring it one step nearer solution—though only for those who avoid the many questions that the juvenile hypothesis leaves unanswered. Acceptance of this kind of interpretation suggests a strong bias on the part of its advocates.

Thus Bolk's concept of the fetalization of the human form raised the deceptive hope that essential processes leading to the emergence of man could be explained in terms of maturation during embryonic development.[29] I myself consider the problem of the evolutionary emergence of torsion—and of man—as unsolved as before.

We shall now look at another aspect of opisthobranchiate life, namely, the problem of their coloration. Many of these shell-less animals give the impression of having a cryptic or semantic coat. In the first case, the effect is evident. However, among the cryptic forms are some that have escaped the searching eye of biologists for close to seventy years, for instance, those green mollusks that are almost indistinguishable from their host, the green alga *Halimeda*.[30] The so-called semantic forms pose a much more difficult problem—they cannot serve the purpose of sexual attraction because the eyes of opisthobranchs cannot form images. Could these patterns be directed at enemies? In other words, are they survival mechanisms?

Now, all the experiments suggest that opisthobranchia are either completely unpalatable or tasteless to fishes. This repulsive effect is probably produced by such structures as glands, spines, nettle cells, etc. Hence it might be argued that fishes learn to avoid all highly colored species. However, since even cryptic species are avoided, this explanation does not hold water.[31]

But even if it did, we must still ask how so many different patterns and colors arose in the first place—what is the formal significance of each. The Opisthobranchia therefore confront us with the same problem as *Micrurus*. Even if we grant the presence of optical selection effects, we still have to say why one pattern rather than another should be offered for selection.

What is true of the fabulous world of marine snails is also true of animal forms in general. Everywhere, patterns can be shown to have a potential selective significance, but the selective effect is usually restricted to a general pattern and only very rarely to the specific differences between patterns of the same type.

Experimental studies have shown that the response to a given formal value persists even when that value has been subject to very considerable deformations, indeed, the distorted value may have the maximum effect. Even if selection favors the preservation of semantic forms, we still know little about the specific meaning of different semantic patterns. Formal studies introduce questions which the theory of selection, even if we were to accept it in full, cannot possibly answer.

This allegation will, of course, be challenged by those biologists who hold that mutations have purely "accidental" effects in the apparative stage.

Now, if by accidental effects they mean no more than that a given structure did not arise for a given functional purpose, we must absolutely agree with them—we do not hold that the pattern, or the notum structure, of opisthobranchia arose "in order to produce a warning effect." This is disproved by every colored pattern and by every one of the complicated notum structures underlying them. But no "accidental" effect can explain why, in *Aegirus,* for instance, metallic blue points should be distributed over the entire body in fixed number and fixed order, and why each point should be embedded in a "cushion" of dark velvet which sets the blue points off like so many jewels. In *Trinchesia,* the color of the spadix is the combined result of blue epidermal structures and a darker contribution by the liver—a combination that is only at work in the visible part of the spadix and which is enhanced by the presence of orange borders on top and below, which, in turn, are formed in the visible region alone, and whose orange is a structural effect of the epidermal cells. These spadices form a complex system that is part and parcel of the self-expression of *Trinchesia coerulea*, a system which, in its formal peculiarity, serves the manifestation of an unaddressed, direct phenomenon.

There are countless further examples of such complex pattern-forming systems—our marine collections abound with them. Their possible selection value may explain their preservation but never their form, and to call them all chance products is tantamount to admitting the failure of the powers of rational explanation or to denying the obvious existence of a co-ordinating principle.

The whole subject impinges on the theory of evolution to which we can now turn our full attention.

VII.

Evolution

The Transformation of Living Forms in Geological Time

THE IDEA of the gradual development of life on earth was the basic premise of all my arguments so far, even though I have emphasized certain shortcomings in the current approach to evolution. We shall now look at these shortcomings at some greater length.

The mystery of the evolution of life is part of a greater mystery—the evolution of the Universe. Just as, four hundred years ago, Western man was forced to revise his view that the earth is the center of the Universe, so he had to make an even more radical break with the past a hundred years ago when he was forced to accept that life on earth is the result of gradual transformations.[1]

True, the idea itself was not entirely original, but only Darwin's combination, in 1859, of a weighty mass of evidence with the simple concept of sexual selection, could lead to that great mental revolution to which we are heir today.[2]

Darwin's ideas were at once seized upon by politicians, to be turned into ammunition not only for late nineteenth century socialist and liberal attacks on the established order but also for colonial expansionism, and later for totalitarianism.[3] Still, it is not the political and social aspects of Darwinism—

however significant—which interest us in this survey, but merely its relevance to those basic biological problems with which this book is primarily concerned.

It is now a century since Darwin's *On the Origin of Species* first appeared to pave the way for the almost universal adoption of the doctrine which Wallace and Darwin promulgated in 1858. Soon after 1900, however, geological studies led to a rejection of some of Darwin's earlier ideas. Lyell's estimate that distinct rock formations represent intervals of 230 million years had to be reduced, even in Darwin's own lifetime, first to a hundred, then to twenty, and in certain cases even to ten million years.[4]

But times change. In the 1930's the figure was increased—and for many good reasons—to 500 million years, and this gave the biologists all the time they needed—much more, in fact, than Darwin had counted on. At about the same time, genetic research led to a radical modification of other Darwinian ideas, to which we shall return later. For the moment, we shall merely say that, ever since 1930, a new doctrine—neo-Darwinism—has come to the fore.

The problem of the origin and development of living organisms is a lifetime study for the individual biologist, and an endless task for biology as a whole. In what follows I shall merely use that problem to sound my own position.

During the century which has gone by since the appearance of Darwin's decisive work, biologists have accumulated an impressive store of biological facts, all of which corroborate the view that every one of the countless organic forms we meet is the result of the self-differentiation of living matter which, in the course of geological time, produces ever-new forms by transformation of the old. In this survey, we shall merely recall a few findings that support this view.

There is first of all the striking fact of the formal relationship between organisms, a relationship which our "natural system" of classification tries to take into account, and which, even before Darwin's time, posed the problem of the "metamorphosis of organic types." Then there is the fact of morphological correspondence, *i.e.* the fact that such apparently unlike structures as wings and arms are derived from one and the same primitive structure. Paleontology joins comparative morphology in showing how existing forms have evolved over thousands of millennia, while the study of the domestication of animals and plants provides evidence of living transformations in relatively short periods. Last but not least, evolutionary processes can now be studied in the laboratory where some of nature's own mutations can be induced artificially.

All these facts and findings corroborate the general theory of evolution, and its wide acceptance reflects the tremendous transformation which our biological and physical views have undergone during the late nineteenth century.

In the early nineteenth century, Alexander von Humboldt still held that the problem of the origin and development of life fell outside the province of natural science, but by 1859, Darwin no longer met great resistance when he tried to show that evolution is a scientific fact.

The difference is more than a mere change in point of view, more than a mere addition of one bit of evidence to an otherwise unchanged philosophical approach—it represents an intellectual revolution of unprecedented scope, and a vast extension of our control over natural processes. Every discussion of the validity of evolution is a discussion of our ability to change living forms. Thus variation experiments in the laboratory merely try to repeat what every flower garden displays in such natural profusion and what paleontological finds demonstrate with so many striking examples.

We do not have to discuss the degree of certainty which philosophers attribute to such biological statements. Nevertheless, we must emphasize that their force rests largely on the fact that the general theory of evolution makes no special statements about the transforming forces involved.

Thus, only by distinguishing his general theory from his special theory of evolution—which was a mixture of primitive thought and commonsense—can we form a correct view of the real contribution of Lamarck.[5] Whereas Lamarck's general theory—that nature, in bringing forth all kinds of animals, improved their organization gradually—provided an explanation of the profusion of living forms which we try to fit into our natural system, and thus built a bridge between eighteenth and nineteenth century thought, his special theory merely obscured the real problem.

Darwin was right to reject Lamarck's special theory, though it is generally forgotten today how much his own thought was tinged with Lamarckian ideas—a large work could be written on "Darwin the Lamarckian." These unconscious "lapses" of Darwin into the outmoded thought of his predecessor were more than isolated attacks of weakness. They recur time and again as the tacit admission of the existence of hidden aspects of life into which his selection theory could not probe.

It was to prove a general theory of evolution, and not any special doctrine, that Darwin, first aboard the *Beagle* and later during the preliminary examination of the material he had gathered, began to look for evidence in favor of the transformation of species. What data he gathered on this journey to suggest the existence of a struggle for existence were no more than fleeting impressions at the time.

A significant change occurred in about 1833, when Darwin first read Malthus's "Essay on Population," and renounced the general theory of evolution in favor of a special theory involving special forces—"my theory" as he came to call it. This change was a gain and a loss at one and the same time: a gain, because it introduced concrete ideas about the transformations involved, thus opening up a vast new field of biological research even in Darwin's day; a loss, because Darwin's special theory became inseparably linked with the general theory of evolution, so much so that the latter was thought to stand or fall by the former.

The new factor which Darwin introduced was the survival of the fittest in the struggle for existence. This concept lent itself to dangerous implications from the start, though Darwin himself kept stressing the "purely metaphorical" nature of his formulation. Yet this aspect of natural selection is the only aspect of Darwinism which has survived all changes, and the only purely "Darwinian" component of neo-Darwinism. Those who identify neo-Darwinism with selection theory are therefore absolutely right.

The causes of the transformations which make selection

possible in the first instance were among Darwin's greatest headaches, and his theory did, in fact, fail to provide a satisfactory answer. What later Darwinists adduced as causes—mutations—Darwin himself considered a secondary phenomenon. True, in his later years he paid more attention to this potential cause of living transformations, but he never accepted it as the solution of the variation problem, which continued to dog his footsteps to the end of his life—Mendel's partial solution was not known to Darwin or his contemporaries.

The great discovery that sudden genetic changes—*i.e.* mutations—in the cell nucleus are a "constant" characteristic of life has led to a new formulation of the special theory of evolution: the different results of mutation supply the material needed for selection. This interpretation has been gaining ground steadily ever since 1920.

Now, mutations can only lead to stable new forms if they are isolated from the original forms by a number of factors. The study of these factors has been proceeding apace during the last few decades, so much so that a new trinity has arisen whose members are selection, mutation, and isolation.

The most crucial of the three is mutation or gene transformation.[6] We distinguish between three main types: 1) sectional mutations involving only parts of chromosomes; 2) mutations involving the translocation, duplication, inversion, etc., of larger blocks of chromosomes or the loss of a portion of the chromosomes; and 3) genome mutations involving the multiplication or division of the entire chromosome stock. All these processes have become part of elementary biological knowledge and their study a central task of genetics.

Now, whenever students of evolution ask geneticists to define the precise role of mutations in evolutionary processes, the answer they get invariably depends on the informant's particular bias. I shall not bother to list all the various shades of opinion on this question,[7] but shall merely cite two extremes.

On the one hand, we have those according to whom evolution is fully explained in terms of chance mutations, *i.e.* in terms of mutations which arise without any immediate connection to their final results. In this view, therefore, mutation itself—and hence evolution as such—is considered an "accidental" process. The philosophical implications of this view are plain for all to see.

At the other extreme are those who consider that what mutations we can study or induce in the laboratory fail to provide an adequate explanation of the successive stages of evolution. While few upholders of this view would deny that experimental mutations can trigger off limited evolutionary processes, they all consider that a large, and often the largest, part of the total processes involved remains unexplained, even if macromutations, megamutations, and ontomutations were postulated in addition to the mutations we can induce in the laboratory.

There is no way of choosing between these two views. We cannot, after all, reconstruct the past in a test tube; all we can hope to do is to build a model of it. Now, the value we attach to all such models depends greatly on the individual approach we use, and quite particularly on our attitude to science—on whether we consider science but one branch of knowledge among many, or whether we look upon it as the apogee of human achievement, as a fitting substitute for religion and aesthetics. According to our viewpoint, therefore, we turn science into the final goal of—or ultimate threat to —human achievement.

Thus many biologists hold that once the evolutive "mechanisms" are known, it behooves us to implement them with the full powers of our intellect, though it is a debatable point how much freedom of choice we have in the matter. It seems to me that those of us who look more closely into the disputes set off by Teilhard de Chardin's ideas of evolution or Julian Huxley's idea of transhumanism are, in fact, looking into so many dark pools.[8]

Technology provides us with the means of inducing mutations—precisely those mutations of which 95 percent are fatal or harmful—and we are told that these mutations hold the key to a better future. Yet views about this future differ so widely, and there is so general a fear of producing harmful rather than beneficial mutations, that few of us would consider this means of improving mankind an unmixed blessing.

I myself do not believe that the principle of evolution is fully explained by any prevailing theory, and I shall briefly explain why. Some of my reasons have emerged in earlier sections of this book, but there are three particular facts to which I should now like to draw quite special attention.

The first is that, as a direct result of the methods it is

forced to employ, genetics is bound to make one-sided statements; simply because the chromosomes and the nucleus are particularly responsive to artificial manipulations, geneticists tend to forget the cytoplasm altogether. Yet experiments in developmental physiology have shown beyond the shadow of a doubt that while the nucleus triggers off cytoplasmic processes, the reverse can also be the case. Hence it is wrong to equate nuclear changes with genetic changes in general. To consider the structure of nucleic acids, whose role we can partly explain, as the "cause" of an animal's specificity is surely no more than a bad lapse into the kind of localization theory which brain research and genetic research have discarded. As long as we continue in our present ignorance of the joint effects of cytoplasm and nucleoplasm, we have no right to exaggerate the role of one element, simply because it is the only one we know.

This brings us to the second fact to which I wish to draw attention. Once we leave the macromolecular stage and arrive at the apparative stage, we meet co-ordinated phenomena which are the *sine qua non* of selection—their presence alone makes selection possible. We have seen that such phenomena as the combination of a large number of feathers into a single optical effect, or the appearance of rhythmical patterns across the bodies of snakes, are all formal effects that cannot be explained by prevailing mutation theories. This criticism does not in any way diminish the real value of experimental attempts to influence the nucleus—genetics has perforce to use the available resources—but is exclusively directed at those who offer the results of mutation research as the whole answer

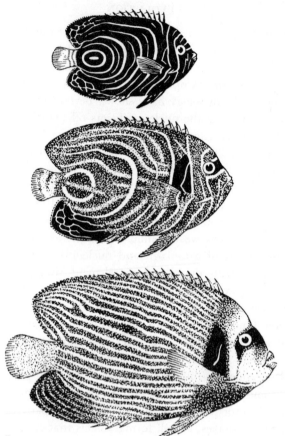

The emperor fish (*Pomacanthus imperator*) which lives among reefs in the Indian and South Pacific Oceans. In the juvenile phase, a purple background bears a pattern of broad white and narrow blue stripes. In adults, the white stripes have disappeared completely, while the blue stripes have straightened out. (After A. Fraser-Brunner.)

to the complex problem of evolution. Now, we have seen that effects like Oudemans' phenomenon, for instance, cannot possibly be considered side effects of "essential" mutations, for no such side effects have ever been produced experimentally. The fact that final patterns arise in four distinct germinal regions is not an argument against the theory of evolution as such but merely against one of its special hypotheses (Fig. 29).

Last but not least—mutation research has to select those problems which, when posed correctly, can provide precise scientific answers. That is its great merit—and its great limitation. Thus mutation research can tell us little about the complex processes that go into the making of the inner world of higher animals.

For instance, it can make no precise statements about processes which ensure the smooth operation by which the optical impressions received by a simple lens are transmitted to a central nervous organization ready to interpret these impressions.[9] The structures involved are again of a degree of complexity, that no experimental mutations have been able to produce.

This, too, is no criticism of the theory of evolution, for no one would deny that psychological structures evolve as well as physiological structures—that is precisely the reason why I have devoted part of this book to the hierarchical problem, and why my own work has been directed at a more precise correlation of cerebralization and evolution. All I object to is the belief that verifiable mutations can explain the origins of complex psychological processes, or the origins of what we have called the self-expression of living forms. All they can explain is that every one of these complex structures is subject to sudden changes with unpredictable results.

Many people, and even some biologists, find it difficult to admit that the mystery of the evolution of life on earth is not yet fully solved—they cannot resist the temptation to explain the unknown whole by its known parts. And yet true knowledge can only spring from an open mind, a mind that is aware of what is still hidden and also of what must remain hidden forever. That type of mind will also have to make a new assessment of the hierarchy of living characters, to which we shall now turn our attention.

VIII.

The Hierarchy of Vital Characteristics

Life as the Combination of Sensibility, Appearance,
and Preservation

THE PROBLEM of the hierarchy of vital characteristics is another which many biologists consider solved once and for all.

Among the many factors which determine our assessment of the importance of vital characteristics, two are particularly marked. The first is our desire to arrive at general laws. It causes us to give greater weight to all those characteristics which biological research can show to be the most readily explicable and the most widespread. This emphasis explains why form and color are so often given second place to digestion, respiration, nerve and muscle functions, and genetic processes. Moreover, the prevalent theory of evolution concentrates on these characteristics because they play a special role in the survival of the species and of the individual.

The second main factor governing our evaluation of vital characteristics reflects our practical preoccupation—we concentrate quite particularly on all those characteristics which we wish to control. This tendency, too, gives particular weight to characteristics which ensure or endanger survival. Tremendous resources are placed at the disposal of this kind of biological research. No wonder it attracts young scientists in increasing number.

Now, as long as we remember that the particular trends by which we assess the significance of vital characteristics impose certain limitations, and that they lead to the neglect of other important aspects of life, all is well.

In the prevalent view, however, all that matters is the survival value of individual characteristics—what does not fit in with this view is called an accidental side-effect, or a dispensable extra. Thus the term *hypertely,* which we use to describe structures that have gone "too far," merely means that the structures have gone beyond the needs of self-preservation. The overdeveloped antlers of the prehistoric stag, the exaggerated size and curvature of the mammoths' tusks, and similar characteristics of extinct creatures, are cited as examples of fatal hypertely. Even psychological structures are judged by their preservation value; thus the human mind is said to be a mere compensation for the loss of primitive survival instincts.

One may perhaps say that biology does no more and no less than its proper task, which is to state what its techniques enable it to state, and only that. Now, there is nothing wrong with this formulation, provided only that the existence of phenomena that do not fit into it is not, for that reason, rejected out of hand.

We have seen that organic life is characterized not only by survival mechanisms but also by what we have called unaddressed phenomena, *i.e.* by phenomena that cannot possibly have any kind of survival value. We have therefore argued that the germ is provided not only with survival structures, but also with phenomenal structures whose importance and number are at least as great. Indeed, it is quite possible that self-expression involves structures whose complexity transcends that of survival mechanisms. In either case, such structures are not occasional exaggerations, but the fulfillment of an important demand of life. An examination of our own existence leads to a similar conclusion: our actions often go far beyond the demands of mere survival.

There are countless examples of how self-preservation and self-expression may combine in one and the same organ. Thus the vocal organ in the trachea of birds serves song production and respiration alike, and our own larynx is a respiratory organ as well as an organ of speech. In addition, song and speech themselves combine self-preservation with self-expression.

But what precisely is the "self" that represents itself to us in so many different ways? It is a living form which has transcended the macromolecular stage to reveal itself at the higher, apparative stage—a living form that not only maintains its life and propagates its kind, but one that also manifests its special manner of existence.

At this stage, living matter has ceased to multiply by constant division of short-lived and simple forms. Instead, we have individuals whose duration of life increases with their level of organization. And with the appearance of the individual, we also have the appearance of death.

Perhaps this great step from the macromolecular to the apparative stage will prove to have been a particularly crucial event in the development of organic life—a leap to a new level of life, rather than one of many small steps in an uninterrupted series of stages. It might well be that the step toward death and the individual was precisely the tremendous step toward self-expression, that external sign of a new level of inner development.

Metabolism may serve the survival of the individual, but however important it is, we must remember that the individual is not there for the sake of its metabolism, but rather that metabolism serves manifest individual existence. That is why the special structures, which we call this plant or that animal, are much more than organized complexes of survival mechanisms (Fig. 30). Thus, while it is true to say that all flowers serve the reproduction of their kind, this statement fails to explain why a given flower should have one form rather than another. In the current view, the structural function alone is considered, and the structural plan is ignored. However, before it can serve any function, the plan itself must be there, and the fact that it varies from species to species deserves much more attention than most biologists seem to pay it.

What I have said of visual phenomena is equally true of acoustical phenomena. Nothing seems more natural than to explain bird song in terms of warning or mating calls, and to forget that this is by no means the whole explanation. Let us return to the song of the garden warbler. Experts tell us that its beautiful spring song is repeated in the autumn when all sexual activity has ceased, and even when the bird is kept in complete solitude.[1] This song is therefore the bird's acousti-

FIG. 30

An examination of the head feathers of the African crowned crane
(*Balearica pavonina*) gives us some idea of the number of genetic
factors that have to combine in the germ to co-ordinate the final "appearance." Some of these factors are exclusively concerned with the
production of white (white is not a pigmentary but a structural color),
others with the production of the black velvet effect (melanines).
The "crown" is the result of special toughening factors, which include
the twisting of every crown feather. In addition, hemoglobin helps to
add to the total effect by coloring the neck-wattles red. Special factors regulate the respective lengths of feathers in different regions. The
"aim" of every one of these feathers is self-representation, and not
flight or heat regulation.

cal means of self-expression—no less so than the characteristic coloration of its plumage.

We have said before that what represents itself to our senses is a particular "self." When we speak of phenomena, we take it for granted that there must be a beholder to whom they appear. This is not only an unavoidable consequence of our language but also of the human condition in general. We cannot speak of the world, or of awareness, of inner responses, or of phenomena, without ourselves and our own experience becoming the presupposition of any statement we make. In short, we cannot imagine phenomena apart from a seeing eye.

That such phenomena nevertheless exist is shown by the occurrence of what we have called unaddressed phenomena. Many of these must have existed before the emergence of the first eye, and yet were examples of self-expression, just like all the many unaddressed phenomena we can observe today. Living creatures were probably never the "physiological bags" which some functional biologists have called them[2]—a rich appearance is always the reflection of a rich inner world.

We must learn to look at the phenomena themselves, at the self-expression of living forms as such, and not only at the role phenomena play in thousands of life's dramas, for instance in mating, flocking, and warning. All these roles must be granted, but the phenomena themselves must be seen as links in a much wider chain, the chain of self-expression.

The living creature confronts us as an entity, and no one can completely detach the survival functions from the rest;

every attempt to do so is an artifice. Thus if we have been stressing the importance of self-expression as the external manifestation of the animal's inner world, we have not forgotten the mighty ties which bind these manifestations of life to the demands of self-preservation. We have remembered that a rich inner life depends largely on relative immunity to environmental changes, and that only relatively autonomous organisms can realize that degree of inner independence, that degree of selfhood, which goes hand in hand with a rich manner of self-expression.

This greater degree of autonomy took hundreds of millions of years to achieve, for it is only when chemical processes inside the organism are stabilized—when there is a constant salt content in the body fluids—that the organism can be said to have attained any degree of independence.

The comparative study of lower animals enables us to follow the gradual emergence of those regulative faculties which, for instance, enable a salmon to survive its annual migration from salt to sea water, or a frog to leave an aquatic for a terrestrial environment.

Next comes thermal independence—the emergence of animals capable of regulating their body heat—which finds its highest expression in the two great classes of warm-blooded animals: mammals and birds.

Heat regulation—that milestone in the evolution of life—is a reminder of the heavy demands that are made on all higher forms of life. Higher life is not only a richer form of life but also a much more precarious form of life. Thus animals which keep their body temperatures constant require a constant supply of food—their higher temperature enables them to survive the rigors of winter and ice, but not of prolonged starvation. This is precisely the reason why so many birds breed in the Arctic or Antarctic where the oceans teem with nourishment.

I am stressing this dependence on the environment, and the importance of metabolic processes in general, because they are so important in the life of all higher organisms. No account of evolution can afford to ignore them—just as it cannot ignore those processes which serve the animal's self-expression.

Self-expression as the measure of inner development, and as the highest expression of life, provides us with a new criterion of assessing levels of vitality.

We cannot use inner development itself as a direct criterion, for our knowledge of psychological processes decreases as we move down the scale of life, on which we occupy the top rung. But as we have seen, the inner world of even macromolecular structures can speak to us through its external manifestations.

The mere fact that we cannot translate this speech into human words is no reason for denying the manifestations themselves. If I watch a foreign play of which I cannot understand a single word, I do not claim that no play is being performed, or that what I see are random gestures.

The view that self-expression is based on innate structures and innate behavior patterns calls for a re-examination of the objects of morphology. It calls, above all, for a new discussion of the connection between form and function. This discussion leads us back to a question which we posed in our earlier discussion of the technical interpretation of organic forms.

The concept of the unity of form and function has had so seductive an effect on many biologists that they have turned it into a slogan. But however fruitful functional morphology has been, and will undoubtedly remain, it has certain limits which are imposed by the way in which we define the term "function." If we reject all but those functions that can be fitted into the framework of survival mechanisms, then many vital structures are necessarily omitted from scientific research. Just as we have tried to show throughout this book that a host of structures and behavior patterns cannot be explained in these terms, so we must now emphasize that the task of morphology goes far beyond the study of "functions" in the narrow sense of the word. It is no accident that systematic botanists and zoologists encounter a host of characteristics in their work which have a "purely" taxonomic or a "purely" systematic significance.

Instead of excluding so much from functional morphology, it might be far better to extend the concept of vital function to include what we have called the self-expression of living forms. This is, of course, a matter for discussion—far be it from me to prejudge the issue when we are just beginning to elaborate a new conception of organic life. But, whatever the outcome, morphology is more than the study of those forms whose function is fully understood or even of those forms which—as biologists used to say—"are not yet explained by physiology." In short, morphology must explode the present framework of purely physiological interpretations.

In any case, there is no reason why we should not establish a hierarchy in which preservation structures and processes are distinguished from another, sovereign group: sensibility and inner potential as reflected by external self-expression. If I propose the adoption of the latter as criteria of vital levels it is not only because they include structures that are usually ignored, but also because the elaboration of the new system poses special questions that lead us to the very limits of science.

The necessity of advancing to these limits and of looking beyond them is imposed on the biologist not least because his work leaves an ever-growing mark on daily life. Whenever a biologist supplies the physician with new drugs, whenever he has to eliminate harmful animals or plants, or transplants species from one region to another, he invariably has to make decisions involving the hierarchy of vital characteristics. That this decision enters even when he has to determine which aspects of life are scientifically explicable and which are not, I hope to have made clear in this book. Whenever we forget that scientific statements have a limited scope, we necessarily reduce life to the level of our technical grasp.

Many recent trends in technology itself point to the need of a wider conception of life. Thus cybernetics does far more than provide clever imitations of complex living structures— it takes us to the realm beyond technology, to the living organism, in which alone the processes which cybernetics tries to copy can arise.

Even the "liveliest" robot has the arbitrary form that its constructor has chosen for it, and obeys his will. It remains a part of man. The most modest plant, however, expresses its independent being in the form of its leaf, flower, and fruit, as does the butterfly in its larva, pupa, and imago. Those marine snails which are seen by no eye except that of the occasional human explorer, express their essence in a host of splendid forms and colors—each according to its kind. Their appearance speaks a language of which we suspect we can grasp a few words, and gives evidence of a hidden power of life, that goes far beyond the needs of mere self-preservation.

Notes

I. Invisible Life

1. Kuhn, W., *Die Gestalt grosser Moleküle als Beispiel für das Wesen spezieller und allgemeiner Forschung.* Basler Universitätsreden, Vol. 36, 1955. Schmidt, W. J., *Der molekulare Bau der Zelle.* Nova Acta Leopoldina, Vol. 7, No. 45, 1939. Staudinger, H., *Makromolekulare Chemie und Biologie.* Basle, 1947.

2. Frey-Wyssling, A., *Elektronen-Mikroskopie.* Vierteljahresschr. Naturforschd. Ges. Zürich, Vol. 95, No. 4, 1951. Pantin, C. F. A., *Living Machinery and the Electron Microscope.* Brit. Assoc. for the Advancement of Science, No. 60, March 1959.

3. Miescher, J. F., *Die histochemischen und physiologischen Arbeiten.* Leipzig, 1897. Joh. Friedr. Miescher (1844–95) lectured in physiology at Basle and was a co-founder of cellular chemistry.

4. Wieser, W., *Gewebe des Lebens.* Bremen, 1959.

5. Clark, F., and Synge, R. L. M. (ed.), *The Origin of Life on the Earth.* Intern. Union of Biochem. Sympos. Series, Vol. 1, London, 1959.

6. Darlington, C. D., *Evolution of Genetic Systems.* Edinburgh and London, 1958. Dobzhansky, Th., *Die Entwicklung zum Menschen.* Hamburg and Berlin, 1955.

7. Wieser, W., *Organismen, Strukturen, Maschinen.* Frankfurt, 1959.

II. The Whole and Its Parts

1. Moser, F., "Siphonophora," *Handbuch der Zoologie,* Vol. 1, Pt. 2, 1923–25.

2. Berill, N. Y., *Growth, Development and Pattern.* San Francisco and London, 1961. Bonner, J. T., *The Cellular Slime Molds.* Princeton, 1950. Pavillard, J., *Ordre des Mycétozoaires.* Traité de Zoologie, Vol. 1, Fasc. II, 1953. Pavillard, J., *Ordre des Acrasiés.* Traité de Zoologie, Vol. I, Fasc. II, 1953.

3. Heidenhain, M., *Plasma und Zelle.* Jena, 1902, 1910.

4. Reith, F., *Die Entwicklung des Musca-Eies nach Ausschaltung verschiedener Eibereiche*. Zeitschr. f. wissensch. Zoologie, Vol. 126, H. 2/3, 1925.

5. Lillie, F. R., *Differentiation without cleavage in the eggs of the Annelid Chaetopterus*. Arch. f. Entw. Mech., Vol. 14, 1906.

6. Spemann, H., *Experimentelle Beiträge zu einer Theorie der Entwicklung*. Berlin, 1936.

7. Duboscq, O., and Grassé, P., *L'appareil parabasal des Flagellés*. Archives de Zoologie expérimentale et générale, Vol. 73, Fasc. 3, 1933. Grassé, P., *Ordre des Trichomonadines*. Traité de Zoologie, Vol. I, Fasc. I, 1952. Grassé, P., *Ordre des Trichonymphines, ibid*. Grassé, P., *Ordre des Spirotrichonymphines, ibid*.

8. Seidel, F., Bock, E., and Krause, G., *Die Organisation des Insekteneies*. Die Naturwissenschaften, Vol. 28, 1940. Seidel, F., *Untersuchungen über das Bildungsprinzip der Keimanlage im Ei der Libelle Platycnemis pennipes I-V*. Roux' Archiv f. Entwicklungsmechanik, Vol. 119, 1929.

9. Duboscq, O., *Discours de M. O. Duboscq, Président d'Honneur*. Bull. de la Société zoologique de France, Vol. LXIV, 1939.

10. Hartmann, M., *Die Sexualität*. Jena, 1943.

III.   The Inner World

1. Daumer, K., *Blumenfarben, wie sie die Bienen sehen*. Zeitschr. f. vergl. Psychologie, Vol. 41, 1958. v. Frisch, K., *Aus dem Leben der Bienen*. Verständliche Wissenschaft, Vol. 1, 5th ed., Berlin, 1953. v. Frisch, K., *"Uber den Farbensinn der Insekten,"* in *Mechanisms of Colour Discrimination*. London, 1960.

2. Kramer, G., *Die Sonnenorientierung der Vögel*. Verhandlg. Deutsch. Zool. Ges., Freiburg, 1952.

3. Sauer, F., *Die Sternorientierung nächtlich ziehender Grasmücken*. Zeitschr. f. Tierpsychologie, Vol. 14, 1957. Sauer, F. and E., *Nächtliche Zugorientierung europäischer Vögel in Südwestafrika*. Die Vogelwarte, Vol. 20, No. 1, 1959. Merkel, F. W., and Fromme, H. G., *Untersuchungen über das Orientierungsvermögen nächtlich ziehender Rotkehlchen (Erithacus rubecula)*. Die Naturwissenschaften, Vol. 20, 1958.

4. Papi, F., *Experiments on the Sense of Time in Talitrus saltator (Montagu) (Crustacea-Amphipoda)*. Experientia, Vol. XI/5, 1955.

5. Griffin, D. R., "More about Bat 'Radar,'" *Scientific American,* July, 1958. Kulzer, E., *Untersuchungen über die Biologie von Flughunden der Gattung Rousettus Gray*. Z. Morph. u. Oekol. d. Tiere, Vol. 47, 1958. Kulzer, E., *Flughunde erzeugen Orientierungslaute durch Zungenschlag*. Die Naturwissenschaften, Vol. 5, 1956. Möhres, F. P., *Die Ultraschall-Orientierung der Fledermäuse*. Die Naturwissenschaften, Vol. 12, 1952.

6. Möhres, F. P., *Elektrische Entladungen im Dienste der Revierabgrenzung bei Fischen*. Die Naturwissenschaften, Vol. 44, 1957. Lissmann, H. W., and Machin, K. E., *The Mechanism of Object Location in Gymnarchus niloticus and Similar Fish*. Journal of Experimental Biology, Vol. 35, 1958. Lissmann, H. W., *On the Function and Evolution of Electric Organs in Fish*. Journ. Experim. Biology, Vol. 35, 1958.

7. Koehler, O., *Vom unbenannten Denken*. Verhandlg. Deutsch. Zool. Ges., Freiburg, 1952.

8. Von Uexküll, Jacob, *Streifzüge durch die Umwelten von Tieren und Menschen*. Bedeutungslehre. Hamburg, 1956.

9. Buytendijk, F. J. J., *Mensch und Tier*. Hamburg, 1958. Lorenz, K., *Der Kumpan in der Umwelt des Vogels*. Journal f. Ornithologie 83, 1935. Tinbergen, N., *Curious Naturalists*. London, 1958. Tinbergen, N., *The Study of Instinct*. Oxford, 1951.

10. Sauer, F., *Die Entwicklung der Lautäusserungen vom Ei ab schalldicht gehaltener Dorngrasmücken*. Zeitschr. f. Tierpsych., Vol. 11, 1954. Thorpe, W. H., *The Learning of Song Patterns by Birds, with Special Reference to the Song of the Chaffinch* Fringilla coelebs. *Ibid.,* Vol. 100, 1958.

11. Wieser, W., *Organismen, Strukturen, Maschinen*. Frankfurt/M., 1959.

12. Roux, W., *Das Wesen des Lebens*. Allgemeine Biologie. In: Kultur der Gegenwart. Leipzig, 1915. Wilh. Roux (1850–1924) was a founder of experimental embryology.

13. Fox, D. L., *Animal Biochromes and Structural Colours*. Cambridge, 1953. Fox, M. H., and Vevers, G., *The Nature of Animal Colours*. London, 1960.

IV. Natural Form and Technical Shape

1. Darwin, Ch., *A Monograph of the Cirripedia*. Two volumes. London, 1851, 1854. Darwin's scrupulous investigations in a number of fields have helped to gain him the authority on which the success of his main thesis was so largely based. His study of the cirripedes is an impressive witness of his thoroughgoing approach. This is what M. M. Huxley wrote to Darwin's son:

> In my opinion your sagacious father never did a wiser thing than when he devoted himself to the years of patient toil which the Cirripede-book cost him. Like the rest of us, he had no proper training in biological science, and it has always struck me as a remarkable instance of his scientific insight that he saw the necessity of giving himself such training, and of his courage, that he did not shirk the labour of obtaining it.

2. Sullivan, L. (1856–1924), American architect. Cf. Roth, A., *Zeitgemässe Architekturbetrachtungen,* Das Werk, Vol. 10, 1947.

3. Metzger, W., *Gesetze des Sehens*. Senckenberg-Buch 33, Frankfurt, 1953.

4. Wölfflin, H., "Die Kunst der Renaissance," *Italien und das deutsche Formgefühl*. Munich, 1931. Wölfflin, H., *Gedanken zur Kunstgeschichte*. Basle, 1940. Heinrich Wölfflin (1864–1945), art historian (Basle, Berlin, Munich, Zurich).

5. Kirchhoff, R., "Uber Physiognomik und Pathognomik." Jahrbuch für Psychologie und Psychotherapie, Vol. H.3/4, 1957. Kirchhoff, R., *Allgemeine Ausdrucklsehre*. Göttingen, 1957. Freudenberg, G., "Zum philosophischen Begriff der Funktion," in *Beiträge zu Philosophie und Wissenschaft*. Munich, 1960.

V. The Hierarchy of Living Forms

1. Wölfflin, H., "Die Kunst der Renaissance," *Italien und das Deutsche Formgefühl*. Munich, 1931, p. 111.

2. Dubois, E., *Sur le rapport du poids de l'encéphale avec la grandeur du corps chez les Mammifères*. Bull. Soc. Anthrop. Paris, 4th ed., Vol. 8, 1897. Lapicque, L., *Le poids de l'encéphale dans les différents groupes d'Oiseaux*. Bull. Mus. Hist. Nat., Vol. 15, Paris, 1909. Edinger,

T., *Die Paläoneurologie am Beginn einer neuen Phase*. Experientia, Vol. VI/7, 1950.

3. Wirz, K., *Zur quantitativen Bestimmung der Rangordnung bei Säugetieren*. Acta Anatomica, Vol. IX, 1950. Wirz, K., *Ontogenese und Cerebralisation bei Eutheria*. Acta Anatomica, Vol. XX, 1954. Rensch, B., "The Relation between the Evolution of Central Nervous Functions and the Body Size of Animals," in Huxley, Hardy, Ford, *Evolution as a Process*. London, 1954.

4. Portmann, A., *Etudes sur la Cérébralisation chez les oiseaux*. I. Introduction. Alauda, XIV, 1946. II. Les indices intra-cérébraux. Alauda, XV-1, 1947. III. Cérébralisation et mode ontogenétique. Alauda, XV-2, 1947. Portmann, A., *Die allgemeine biologische Bedeutung der Cerebralisations-Studien*. Bull. der Schweiz. Akad. d. Med. Wissensch., Vol. 8, 1952. Portmann, A., *Zur Gehirnentwicklung der Säuger und des Menschen in der Postembryonalzeit*. Bull. der Schweiz. Akad. d. Med. Wissensch., Vol. 13, 1957. Stingelin, W., *Vergleichend-morphologische Untersuchungen am Vorderhirn der Vögel auf cytologischer und cytoarchitekonischer Grundlage*. Basle, 1958.

5. Ratzerdorfer, C., *Volumetric Indices for the Parts of the Insect Brain. A Comparative Study in Cerebralization of Insects*. Journal of the New York Entomological Society, Vol. LX, 1952. Wirz, K., *Etude Biométrique du Système Nerveux des Céphalopodes*. Bulletin Biologique de la France et de la Belgique, Vol. XCIII, 1959.

VI. The Realm of Images

1. *The Self-Expression of Living Forms*

1. The central theme of this chapter is discussed in: Portmann, A., *Um ein neues Bild vom Organismus*. In: *Offener Horizont*. Festschr. f. Karl Jaspers, Munich, 1953. Portmann, A., *Die Erscheinung der lebendigen Gestalten im Lichtfelde*. In: Wesen und Wirklichkeit des Menschen. Festschr. f. Helmuth Plessner. Göttingen, 1957. Portmann, A., *Unterwegs zu einem neuen Bild vom Organismus*. In: Die Welt in Neuer Sicht. Munich, 1957. Portmann, A., *Transparente und opake Gestaltung*. In: Rencontre; Festschrift für F. J. J. Buytendijk. Utrecht/Antwerp, 1957.

2. Portmann, A., *Die Tiergestalt*, 2nd Ed. Basle, 1960. This is my most comprehensive work on the problem of form.

3. Portmann, A., *Goethes Naturforschung.* Neue Schweizer Rundschau, Vol. H. 7, 1953.

2. *The Interpretation of Animal Patterns*

1. Oudemans, J. Th., *Etude sur la position du repos chez les Lépidoptères.* Verh. Kon. Akad. Wetensch., Sect. II, Vol. 10, 1903.

2. Portmann, A., *Animal Camouflage.* Ann Arbor, 1959.

3. Schwanwitsch, B. N., *Evolution of the Wing-Pattern in Palaearctic Satyridae.* Zeitschr. Morph. u. Oek. d. Tiere, Vol. 21, 1931.

4. Goodwin, T. W., *Carotenoids and reproduction.* Biol. Reviews, 25, 1950. Goodwin, T. W., *Carotenoids in Fish.* Biochem. Soc. Symposia, 6, 1951. Steven, D. M., *Studies on Animal Carotenoids, II. Carotenoids in the Reproductive Cycle of the Brown Trout.* Journ. exp. Biology, 26, 1949.

5. Doflein, F., *Lebensgewohnheiten und Anpassungen bei dekapoden Krebsen.* Festschr. f. R. Hertwig, Vol. 3, Jena, 1910.

6. Wigglesworth, V. B., *Insect Physiology.* Methuen's Monographs. London, 1934.

7. Haecker, V., *Entwicklungsgeschichtliche Eigenschaftsanalyse (Phänogenetik).* Jena, 1918. Haecker, V., *Aufgaben und Ergebnisse der Phänogenetik.* Bibliographia Genetica, I, 1925. Lebedinsky, N. G., *Darwins Theorie der geschlechtlichen Zuchtwahl im Lichte der heutigen Forschung.* Bibliographia Genetica, IX, 1932.

8. v. Frisch, K., *Über Zeichnungsmuster auf Schmetterlingsflügeln.* Sitzungsber. Bayerische Akad. d. Wissenschaften, Mathem.-naturw. Kl., 1958.

3. *Snake Patterns*

1. Zenneck, J., *Die Anlage der Zeichnung und deren physiologische Ursachen bei Ringelnatterembryonen.* Zeitschr. f. wiss. Zool., Vol. 58, 1894.

2. Fioroni, P., *Zur Pigment- und Musterentwicklung bei squamaten Reptilien.* Revue Suisse de Zoologie, Vol. 68, 1961.

3. v. Harnack, M., *Die Hautzeichnungen der Schlangen.* Z. Morph. u. Oekol. der Tiere, Vol. 41, 1953. Wolf, K. L., and Wolff, R., *Symmetrie (Textband).* Münster and Cologne, 1956.

4. Mertens, R., *Gibt es eine Mimikry bei Korallenschlangen?* Natur und Volk, Vol. 87, 1957.

5. Magnus, D., *Experimentelle Untersuchungen zur Bionomie und Ethologie des Kaisermantels,* Argynnis paphia L. Zeitschr. f. Tierpsychologie, Vol. 15, 1958. Tinbergen, N., Meeuse, B. J. D., Boerema, L. K., and Varossieau, W. W., *Die Balz des Samtfalters,* Eumenis (= Satyrus) semele L. Zeitschr. f. Tierpsychologie, Vol. 5, 1942.

4. Feathers

1. Becker, R., *Die Strukturanalyse der Gefiederfolgen von Megapodius freyc. reinw. und ihre Beziehung zu der Nestlingsdune der Hühnervögel.* Revue Suisse de Zoologie, Vol. 66, 1959. Frank, F., *Die Färbung der Vogelfeder durch Pigment und Struktur.* Journ. f. Ornithol., Vol. 87, 1939. Sick, H., *Morphologisch-funktionelle Untersuchnungen über die Feinstruktur der Vogelfeder.* Journ. f. Ornithol., Vol. 85, 1937.

2. Brinckmann, A., *Die Morphologie der Schmuckfeder von* Aix galericulata L. Revue Suisse de Zoologie, Vol. 65, No. 34, 1958.

3. Göhringer, R., *Vergleichende Untersuchungen über das Juvenil- und Adultkleid bei der Amsel* (Turdus Merula L.) *und beim Star* (Sturnus vulgaris L.). Revue Suisse de Zoologie, Vol. 58, 1951.

4. Sager, E., *Morphologische Analyse der Musterbildung beim Pfauenrad.* Revue Suisse de Zoologie, Vol. 62, 1955.

5. Beebe, W., *Pheasants, Their Lives and Homes.* New York, 1936.

6. Schenkel, R., *Zur Deutung der Balzleistungen einiger Phasianiden und Tetraoniden.* I., II., Ornithol. Beob., Vol. 53, 1956, Vol. 55, 1958.

5. Marine Snails

1. Lemche, H., and Wingstrand, K. G., *The Anatomy of* Neopilina galatheae. Galathea-Report, Vol. 3, Copenhagen, 1959.

2. Bürgin-Wyss, U., *Die Rückenanhange von Trinchesia coerulea* (Mont.) *Eine morphologische Studie über Farbmuster bei Nudibranchiern.* Revue Suisse de Zoologie, Vol. 68, 1961. Hoffmann, H., *Dr. H. G. Bronn's Klassen und Ordnungen des Tierreichs.* Vol. 3: Mollusca, II Abt.: Gastropoda, Book 3: Opisthobranchia. Leipzig, 1932. European species: Pruvot-Fol, A., *Faune de France.* 58: Mollusques Opisthobranches. Paris, 1954.

3. Hoffmann, *op. cit.* Particularly important are: Naville, A., *Notes sur les Eolidiens.* Revue Suisse de Zool., Vol. 33, 1926. Rousseau, Ch.,

Histophysiologie du Foie des Eolidiens. Arch. Anat. Microsc., Vol. 31, 1935.

4. Fox, D. L., *Animal Biochromes and Structural Colours.* Cambridge, 1953.   Fox, M. H., and Vevers, G., *The Nature of Animal Colours.* London, 1960.

5. de Beer, Sir Gavin, F. R. S., *Embryos and Ancestors,* 3rd ed. Oxford, 1958, S. 57.

6. Thompson, T. E., *The Natural History, embryology, larval Biology and post-larval development of* Adalaria proxima. Philos. Trnsact. R. Soc. London, Ser. B, No. 686, 1958.

7. Bolk, L., *Das Problem der Menschwerdung.* Jena, 1926.

8. Portmann, A., *Bosellia mimetica Trinchese, Opisthobranche retrouvé en Meditérranée.* Vie et Milieu, Vol. IX, fasc. I, 1958.

9. Thompson, T. E., *Defensive acid-secretion in marine Gastropods.* Journ. Marine Biol. Assoc. United Kingd. Vol. 39, 1960.

VII. Evolution

1. Portmann, A., "Der biologische Beitrag zu einem neuen Bild des Menschen." Eranos-Jahrbuch fur 1959, Vol. 28, 1960.

2. Eiseley, L., *Darwin's Century,* New York, 1958.   Himmelfarb, G., *Darwin and the Darwinian Revolution.* London, 1959.   Wyss, W., *Charles Darwin.* Zurich and Stuttgart, 1958.

3. Conrad-Martius, H., *Utopien der Menschenzüchtung.* Munich, 1955.

4. Eiseley, L., *op. cit.,* Chapters III and IX.

5. Jean Baptiste de Monnet, Chevalier de Lamarck, first gained distinction as a botanist, and then turned his attention to the classification of invertebrates. In 1809, he wrote in his *Philosophie zoologique* (1873) that "nature in bringing forth all kinds of animals improved their organization gradually," and that these animals were subject to the influence of their environment, which modified their form and habits. Lamarck's critics fastened on his doctrine of the inheritance of acquired characters, and called the experimental refutation of this doctrine a refutation of Lamarckism in general. However, what strikes me as Lamarck's most important contribution to the theory of evolution is not so much that doctrine, as his doctrine of the tendency towards constant perfection, which Darwin opposed with his selection theory. Darwin and Lamarck

were both mistaken in their assumptions about genetic processes—each in his own way. Only if we consider Lamarck's underlying metaphysical assumptions, can we understand Darwin's "lapses" into Lamarckism.

6. Darlington, C. D., *Evolution of Genetic Systems,* 2nd ed. Edinburgh and London, 1958 (see also 7).

7. Tax, Sol. (ed.): *Evolution after Darwin,* 3 vols. Chicago, 1960. Mayr, E., *Systematics and the Origin of Species.* New York, 1942. Huxley, J. S., *Evolution, The Modern Synthesis.* London, 1942. Huxley, J., Hardy, A. C., Ford, E. B. (ed.), *Evolution as a Process.* London, 1954. Rensch, B., *Neuere Probleme der Abstammungslehre.* Stuttgart, 1947. Cuénot, L., *La genèse des espèces animales,* 3rd ed. Paris, 1932. Dalcq, A. M., *Brèves réflexions d'un embryologiste sur le problème de l'Evolution.* L'Age Nouveau, No. 105, Feb.–Mar. 1959. Grene, M., "The Faith of Darwinism." *Encounter,* Vol. 13, No. 5, 1959. Guyénot, E., *Deux problèmes insolubles de la Biologie transformiste.* Foi et Vérité, XX, 1950. Heuts, M. J., *Theorien und Tatsachen der Biologischen Evolution.* Verh. d. Deutschen Zool. Gesellsch., Freiburg, 1952. Hooykaas, R., *Natural Law and Divine Miracle.* Leyden, 1959. Kälin, J., *Zur Frage der Kausalität in der Makroevolution.* Die Naturwissenschaften, Vol. 1, 46th year, 1959. Ruyer, R., *Les Postulats du Sélectionnisme.* Revue philosophique de la France et de l'Etranger, 1956.

8. Portmann, A., *Der Pfeil des Humanen. (Uber Teilhard de Chardin).* Freiburg, 1960. Huxley, J., *New Bottles for New Wine.* New York, 1958.

9. Ruyer, R., *op. cit.* 7.

VIII. The Hierarchy of Vital Characteristics

1. Sauer, F., *Die Entwicklung der Lautäusserungen vom Ei ab schalldicht gehaltener Dorngrasmücken.* Zeitschr. f. Tierpsych., Vol. 11, 1954.

2. Focillon, H., *La vie des formes.* Paris, 1934.

* *

*

General works bearing on the problems discussed in this book:

Arber, A., *The Mind and the Eye.* Cambridge, 1954. *The Natural Philosophy of Plant Form.* Cambridge, 1950.

Buytendijk, F. J. J., *Anschauliche Kennzeichen des Organischen*. Philosophischer Anzeiger, 2nd year, Vol. 4. Bonn, 1928. *Wege zum Verständnis der Tiere*. Zurich and Leipzig, 1938.

Plessner, H., *Die Stufen des Organischen und der Mensch*. Berlin, 1928.

Köhler, W., *The Place of Value in a World of Facts*. London, 1938.

Matthei, R., *Das Gestaltproblem*. Ergebnisse der Physiologie, Vol. 29, 1929.

Merleau-Ponty, M., *La structure du comportement*. Paris, 1949.

Müller, A., *Die Grundkategorien des Lebendigen*. Monogr. z. Naturphilosophie, Vol. III, 1954.

Ruyer, R., *La genèse des formes vivantes*. Paris, 1958.

Szilasi, W., *Wissenschaft als Philosophie*. Zurich, 1945.

Straus, E., *Vom Sinn der Sinne*. Berlin and Göttingen, 1956.

Thompson, Sir d'Arcy Wentworth, *On Growth and Form*. Cambridge, 1942.

Works by the author:

Einführung in die vergleichende Morphologie der Wirbeltiere, 2nd ed. Basle, 1959.

Zoologie und das neue Bild des Menschen. Hamburg, 1951.

Paperback edition of *Biologische Fragmente zu einer Lehre vom Menschen*. Basle, 1944 (2nd ed., 1951).

Das Tier als soziales Wesen. Zurich, 1953.

Biologie und Geist. Zurich, 1956.

Zur Philosophie des Lebendigen. In: Die Philosophie im XX Jahrhundert. Stuttgart, 1960.

Set in Intertype Baskerville
Composed by York Composition Company, Inc.
Printed by Scranton Litho
Bound by Haddon Craftsmen, Inc.
HARPER & ROW, PUBLISHERS, INCORPORATED